Liberation

A.M. Nicol

Ringwood Publishing

Glasgow

The moral right of the author has been asserted

Issued in 2021

by

Ringwood Publishing

Flat 0/1 314 Meadowside Quay Walk, Glasgow

G11 6AY

www.ringwoodpublishing.com

e-mail: mail@ringwoodpublishing.com

ISBN 978-1-901514-56-8

British Library Cataloguing-in Publication Data

A catalogue record for this book is available from the British Library

Printed and bound in the UK

by Lonsdale Direct Solutions

Acknowledgements

To Ruth McQueeney, Beth Whitelaw, and Chloe Murphy for their meticulous editing, and Donald Findlay for his analytical preface. Thanks, as ever, to Mirian for her continuing support.

Preface

Since I first stepped into the High Court of Justiciary more than 45 years ago, two things have dominated my life. The first; the city of Glasgow, where I work, and the second; Glasgow's murders, which I work in. Now, before criticism rains down upon me, I do not suggest for a moment that the two are synonymous, but, for me, they are closely connected.

I grew up in Fife in the 1950s, where I'd hear and read of tales of life in Glasgow. The city fascinated me. I read of the big ships that were built on the Clyde and the men who built them. I aspired to be able to wear a bowler hat – not because they were favoured by members of the legal profession, but because they were indicative of advancement, of status, in the shipyards. I became a supporter of Rangers FC because my granny told me to, and you always did what your granny told you.

Growing up, my father worked very hard to provide for our family. I never had to worry about luxuries, I was unaware of the word, let alone the concept! However, I always felt safe, and knew that the people around me cared for me and would always protect me. Learning about places like the Gorbals was a shock to my system. By today's standards my family was not very well-off, but life in the Gorbals sounded like real poverty. The stories of the violence, of gangs like 'The Cumbie' and the constant malevolent influence of alcohol made Glasgow seem like an alien world dominated by hard drinking, full of violent men and women who would scare the living daylights out of you just for the hell of it.

By the time I was at secondary school and attending university, I visited Glasgow with some regularity. It was changing. The Gorbals were being modernised, albeit not entirely for the better. The M8 was being driven through the heart of the city, tearing down the evidence of its industrial heart. But I had always imagined that Glasgow had a hard edge to it, and that hard edge was still there.

Glasgow's murders first made an impact on my life as I followed the daily reports from the Glasgow High Court, which were documenting the progress of the trial of the serial killer Peter Manuel, who was eventually hanged in Barlinnie Prison in the July of 1958.

In the post war years, the streets of the Gorbals were as dangerous as they were deprived. They were policed by officers who had to be as tough as the conditions they faced. James Ronald Robertson joined the City of Glasgow Police in late 1945 and was posted to the Gorbals. He was a family man, a good husband and father – a man of apparent principle, a member of the Plymouth Brethren. A man of strong and indeed powerful religious conviction; a liar, a thief, an adulterer, and a cold-hearted killer. This piece of information does not in any way spoil your reading of this book. That Robertson killed Katie* was never really in any doubt. The real questions are why, how, and *was* it murder?

To assist him in avoiding the noose, he had the benefit of an impressive legal team, led by the Dean of the Faculty of Advocates, John (Jock) Cameron KC – the very same man who, as a judge, was to send Manuel to the gallows. He was instructed by the legendary Glasgow solicitor Laurence Dowdall. It is worth noting that none of Robertson's legal team were paid a penny for their services. It was one of the great traditions of the Scottish legal profession that no man would face a murder trial without the benefit of the best possible representation. With the aid of Professor John Glaister, one of the giants of forensic medicine, the Crown case charge was that Robertson had killed Katie by driving a stolen car backwards and forwards over her prone body. In the story, the defence developed a strategy which had two parts: Katie was killed because of an accident – Robertson would give evidence to this effect. He had to be believed. Then, his wife would be called as a witness – she was a decent woman, as innocent in all of this as Katie, and would sway the jury against sending her loyal husband to the gallows.

With the hindsight of history, it would be easy to dismiss this strategy as effective as clutching at an illusory straw in the wind. It had two fundamental flaws. It depended on Robertson impressing the jury as a credible witness. This meant admitting the true nature of his relationship with Katie and doing so in public. Secondly, he had to agree to his wife being called as a witness. Robertson consented to neither. *Liberation* examines and tries to understand Robertson's apparent disregard for the consequence of his performance, or lack thereof, in the witness box, something that baffled his advisers at the time and those who have studied the case since.

Suffice it to say that it is well-nigh impossible for a man like me, with no religious beliefs of any kind, to comprehend the blind faith of another. Personally, I take my chances in this life and will worry about the next one if I am unfortunate enough to encounter it. Would Robertson's God greet him with open and forgiving arms? I doubt it. I rather suspect that even the most forgiving God would have little truck with a remorseless killer, however devout he professed himself to be. Perhaps the best that may be said of PC 138D James R. Robertson is that nothing in his life became him like the leaving of it.

My own first ever High Court appearance was in Glasgow, as Crown Junior to the Advocate Depute, Ranald MacLean. I appeared with him in the very same courtroom in which Manuel had been tried and sentenced to death by Lord Cameron.

Since then, I have gone on to defend hundreds of men,

women, and children charged with the most grievous crime in our law: murder. Many of the trials took place in Glasgow High Court, which was a short stroll from the Gorbals. Every individual was different, and the circumstances of each case totally unique. If there was any semblance of common thread that linked them together, it was that many of them were just ordinary people caught up in extraordinary circumstances. Yet, every now and again, one of them would stand out, either because of the nature of the individual or the crime, or sometimes – as in James Ronald Robertson's case, both. It was and continues to be this aspect of the history of criminal law that holds a fascination over me.

Donald Findlay, Advocate and Queen's Counsel, 2021

*Students of the case will realise that Katie's name has been changed.

Chapter 1

With his tunic removed and collar unbuttoned, the musky odour of heavy male sweat filled the police box. The space inside was cramped, but Robertson had just enough room to make an entry to the log by the light of the bare bulb overhead:

At 12.50 today, a woman was knocked down and fatally injured on Prospecthill Road. The motor car, believed to be a small blue Austin, maybe about ten-horsepower, was driven by a man wearing a light brown Burberry coat. The car did not stop and was last seen driving citywards on Aikenhead Road.

He moved his head back and read the entry again, holding it up to the light as he chewed at the end of the pencil. *How did that sound? Convincing? Or not ...?* Droplets of perspiration ran down his shirt, mingling with damp patches and grubby stains.

Hastily, he added the date and his service number, pointlessly pausing to wipe an oily mark from the logbook in case the CID saw it.

02.10 hours, Friday 28th July 1950, 138D.

Chapter 2

As the sun rose that day, urban blackbirds began their morning lament for the Gorbals. It was sweltering again, and the sun baked the stench of leaking sanitation and back court urine into a cloying melange of human despair. Kids played in back courts with dead rats as their mothers got together to smoke and wash clothes as they dreamt of what could be – of unfulfilled notions of getting out of Nicholson Street for good. Some fooled themselves that cheap vodka and seedy encounters with sweaty, violent men (sometimes their own) was just how it was meant to be. Few escaped and life went on, churning out more problems than answers.

For religious types like 138D Robertson, the whole area was a God-given example of why His way was the true, righteous path, the human zoo of inhabitants put there by God so that upright people could visit, pity, and maybe learn from.

Reports of a road traffic fatality a couple of miles south of the Gorbals reached the day shift CID at Oxford Street Police Office. Just after midnight, a taxi driver on Prospecthill Road had slowed, then stopped, beginning to make out the shape of a body lying in the carriageway on the road ahead. He parked his cab in the middle of the street, leaving the headlights on in the poor sodium lighting. He stepped out of the car and saw that it was the body of a woman lying on her back. Her right leg was grotesquely angled; broken and lying across her left in an obscene, solo street tango. Bone pierced through ripped and bloodied nylon stockings, still clinging to her shoeless feet. He instinctively stepped back, but to leave the scene now would lead to suspicion and blame.

Her cheap dress had split open to reveal a grimy corset

underneath, the final indignity being a death grin lacking several front teeth, and a broken dental plate that lay nearby – a tiny, pink and white serrated sea creature miles from home. The road was eerily quiet. The lighting in Hangingshaw was obscured by a row of mature birch and elm trees, abundant summer foliage blotting out the feeble orange glow of the streetlights. But even in the darkness, he knew. There was no sign of life. An ambulance would not be needed.

The sound of a rumbling exhaust coming towards him gave him purpose. He ran forward, stepping into the roadway, the vehicle's full beams causing him to close his eyes and wave, feverishly. Even if it didn't stop, the driver would avoid the lifeless, distorted corpse in its path. Not that it mattered much now, except to preserve a possible crime scene and any shred of dignity the woman once had.

The old pre-war Riley came to a squeaking halt, 20 yards from the taxi driver. The owner pushed a hinged suicide door open and sprang out as the taxi driver wiped his dripping brow with the back of his hand. 'Thanks for stopping. Get the polis, she's dead!'

The man could see a heap of remains behind the taxi driver, his shadow elongated in the headlights, obscuring the corpse – but illuminating the wet patches of blood around it.

'Christ! What happened to her?'

'Looks like she's been run over. There's blood everywhere. Go and get the polis. Quickly. There's a box at the end of the road they always have their tea in.'

'Right you are.'

The Riley driver noisily engaged first gear and then slowed as he drove by, absorbing the full horror of the scene until it was plunged back into semi-darkness. The taxi driver's eyes adjusting back to the gloom, he stayed on the road until he picked out two light coloured objects lying on the edge of the pavement a few feet from each other. Curious, he walked in a wide arc until he got closer. It was two faux patent leather shoes, one upright and the other on its side, as if the woman had neatly removed them before stepping onto the road. Was it suicide? Why in stockinged feet?

Ten long minutes passed before a police car appeared. Two uniformed officers approached the taxi driver, putting their caps on as they walked towards him.

'Did you find her?' one of them asked officiously.

'Yes, that's my taxi. She was just lying on the road. She looks dead,' he added unnecessarily.

'Have you touched anything?' the other officer asked.

'No, I backed off after I saw she was a goner.'

The first officer got to as close as was advisable. The distinct shit-and-blood smell of death was in the warm night air.

'Stop all traffic, both ways,' he called to his colleague, who went back to the car to radio in for other units.

After they'd taken details of the Riley driver, he was free to leave. As cars and lorries trundled towards the scene a note was made of each driver's name and address. The make of the vehicle and its registration plate was noted too, and a cursory check for dents in bodywork or any smashed lights was carried out on the spot. Who knew? Maybe the hit and run driver would come back to see if his handiwork had been discovered. In between vehicles arriving and turning back, the taxi driver had given his name and address, and a record of what he'd seen was noted by the second officer. He had one final observation to make before he left for home:

'One odd thing, though – when I was waiting for you to get here, I noticed a pair of women's shoes on the kerb over there. She had nothing on her feet when she was run over.'

The first officer shone a torch towards the edge of the pavement throwing a patch of light over the shoes, discarded as if the owner had left them on the sand or at the side of a pool and gone for a midnight swim. Had she been chased from the kerb and run onto the road in her stockinged soles in fright?

A refuse lorry with large sliding push-up doors at either side was stopped as it made its way westwards, along the same side of the road the corpse was on. On being stopped and told to wait, the driver noisily ratcheted the handbrake and the passenger got out and spoke to one of the policemen at the scene.

'We drove by here about half an hour ago and I said to Arthur it looked like there was a body on the road but he said I was havering.'

Hearing what his colleague had said, the driver left his cab and spoke confidentially to the other officer. 'Sammy's always going on like that. He goes to the pictures all the time and thinks it's all true. I decided to carry on and said we'd check it on the way back from Rutherglen, just to keep him happy.'

'Well, I was right, wasn't I? I told you!' Sammy had correctly guessed what his colleague had said about him and was feigning indignance.

'And did you see anything else when you passed the first time?' the officer asked them both.

'Nope, nothing except for the black car.'

'Did you both see it?'

Arthur shook his head. 'All I saw was the car, not the lassie.'

Sammy was more positive. 'I saw both. The black car was facing down that way.' He pointed westwards along the road to where the body was lying.

'So where was the car? Was it near the body?'

'The car was stopped in the road and the body was ten yards behind it,' Sammy said.

'What sort of car was it? Can you say?'

'I think it was a black or dark-coloured Austin.'

Sammy turned to Arthur. 'What do you think?'

'I wasn't paying attention. Sammy here sometimes

imagines things and when we're on night shift together, he often comes away with stuff like this.'

Sammy ignored his driver's dismissive comments but hadn't quite finished saying his piece. 'And another thing. The car had no lights on. Suspicious looking if you ask me. Anyway, the point is, I *knew* I was right!'

It was suspicious looking to others too.

Chapter 3

Weekend nightshifts in the Gorbals were always the worst. Drunk on cheap wine, some men took their pent-up anger out on their wives and kids at home whilst others got into street fights with rival, cut-throat razor wielding gangs. Wives and mothers could only do their best in cramped, insanitary conditions where up to ten families shared a stinking toilet and a family of ten shared a two-bedroom flat.

Officially, police officers were advised to patrol in pairs to provide corroboration in any future court proceedings, but in truth the directive had been issued for their safety as much as anything else.

Before joining the force, Police Constable James Ronald Robertson had been dissatisfied working as an engineer and had confided as much in fellow Plymouth Brethren after their Sabbath service. The Brothers then convened a further meeting to discuss how the Lord would best be served by one of their number changing his occupation. At the weekly Lord's Supper, most of the men present agreed that serving as a police officer would give the Lord a real chance to reach out to non-believers. 'Remember, James,' a respected Brother told him, 'the blood of Jesus Christ cleanses us from all sin. He will grant you access to a wicked world full of non-believers, wherever you go. You can do good by teaching the Heathen masses in this city how to make their hearts pure before God.'

There was rejoicing in the gospel hall when James announced his first posting: the infamous Gorbals. A real opportunity to spread the truths of the Holy Bible amongst an unenlightened and ignorant throng.

And so it came to pass that I, James Ronald Robertson, with the support of my fellow Brethren, all of whom have been born within the boundaries of the Covenant of Promise, joined the City of Glasgow Police on 17th November 1945 as a trial of my Faith and in order to encounter and confront those spotted with the leprosy of sin and beyond the pale of the Covenant, those froward masses doomed to everlasting destruction and whom the blood of atonement can never reach. He hath granted me the power of glorious discernment between good and evil and by His Grace the means to tend to the castaways of this world. The Lord sayeth there is a time for everything, a time to search and a time to give up searching and He will bring into judgement both the righteous and the wicked, for there will be a time for everything, a time to judge every deed. He tests us so that we may see we are like animals and our fate is as of animals, as one dies so dies the other, all of them going to the same place, as all come from dust and to dust all return.

The violence, the poverty, the dirt, the hopelessness and the drunkenness were all beyond his imagining. His wife Janice often saw her pious husband retreating to their bedroom to read the Scriptures after yet another day's toil that demanded the Lord's understanding and guidance.

And that was how James Ronald Robertson became Police Constable 138D in The City of Glasgow Police, Southern Division, and how he found himself walking alone in Nicholson Street, deep in the heart of the slums of Glasgow's Gorbals at 2a.m. on Saturday, 16th July 1949. He and his colleague, Police Constable Morison, had already broken up a knife fight outside a pub and quieted a neighbour dispute, all parties drunk to insensibility and window frames in both flats now absent of glass. Morison had gone back to the office at Oxford Street to bind a hand wound before returning to duty and Robertson had fought manfully onwards on his own. At six feet two inches and broad of shoulder, he was a giant amongst a population of malnourished bantams riddled with rickets and foetal alcohol syndrome and so had little fear of doing his duty.

'Hey, you! Mister! You, polisman!' shouted a woman from an open window one floor up, her arms resting on a pillow for comfort during her regular nightly vigil, spying on the many weekend goings on in the street outside. Robertson looked up and just made out an elderly woman smoking a cigarette. He recognised her as a local busybody.

'Aye, what is it, Isa?'

She tossed the still lit stub into the weeds and discarded tin cans outside the flat below, its downward path traced in the darkness like a tiny falling red star. 'There's been a terrible racket from the next close.' She flicked her head to the right as she spoke. 'Sounded a real battle. Died down a bit now. You manage on yer own, son, or are ye gonie wait for reinforcements?'

'I'll manage. You mean number 139?'

'Aye,' she said contentedly. 'Middle floor, name on the door's "Murphy". You lot'll know there's always trouble at weekends with that Murphy woman and her good time men friends. And you can tell her that from me!' she announced decisively, disappearing back inside the darkened room and pulling the window down to emphasise her disdain.

Robertson made his way up the stairs two at a time, noises of raised voices getting ever closer until he stood at the door with the name chalked on it, the white lettering contrasting with faded black paint which was peeling at the edges of dents and gouges telling of previous angry exchanges or attempted break-ins down the years. The male voices inside had subsided to an almost normal level, but a shrill female tone still suggested distress. Robertson tried the cracked round plastic handle which remained surprisingly tight and unyielding, then hammered on the door with the side of his fist. The voices stopped, footsteps padding down the bare floorboards of the lobby towards the door.

'Fuck off back to yer own close, ya auld witch,' an irate male shouted.

'Police, open the door!' Robertson bellowed back.

'What do *you* lot want?' The voice sounded derisive, as if its owner had previous bad experiences with the law.

Robertson had learned that to back down now would be a loss of face and it was time to raise the stakes.

'Just open the door before I break it down!' he demanded.

The voice responded after a few seconds, at the same time as the sound of a key turning in the lock.

'Alright, keep yer hair on!'

The door was opened by a young man aged about twenty-five. He was holding a bottle of cheap sherry wine labelled 'VP' by the neck – known locally as "Virgin's Pish" – and was wearing trousers and a grubby stained vest. He had no shoes on and his dark coloured socks had vibrant patches of green, blue and red where they had been darned down the years. Like many in the area, he was small and bow legged but had an unpredictable anger fuelled at the sight of a police uniform.

'Right, big man – what's the problem?' he asked belligerently.

Robertson towered a foot above him, wary of where the bottle might be headed. Better to defuse things now the door had been opened.

'What's all the shouting about then?' Robertson's tone had altered from demanding to inquisitive.

The man took a swig from the bottle then smiled, displaying gaps and a few yellow brown teeth. 'Listen, is that auld bat Isa causing trouble again?'

Robertson walked into the hall, ignoring the question and the damp stench. 'Do you live here?'

'No, me and my mate are up seeing Katie and Rena. You know, for a good time.' The man traced the outline of a woman despite still holding the bottle in his right hand.

A woman in her late thirties appeared in the hall. She was wearing a cheap silver nylon dressing gown which matched a pair of tattered silver high heels. Her dyed blonde hair was piled up on her head in a beehive and she was smoking a cigarette through a long plastic silver holder which had brassy red lipstick stains at the base.

Star gazing from the gutter.

'Thanks for coming up, Officer. Matthew and his pal are just leaving,' she said authoritatively.

The man looked annoyed. 'Are we? You said we could …'

'Never mind what I said,' she interrupted sharply, 'You had better get out now or I'll get this officer to lift the pair of you.' She went back into the front room and summoned Robertson to follow her, repeatedly bending the index finger of her right hand until he complied. Once there he saw another, younger male wearing brothel creepers and tight trousers, his dark hair Brylcreemed into a quiff, a *DA* at the back. He had an obvious scar on his right cheek and was drinking a dark brown coloured liquid from a jam jar. He was clearly startled to see a policeman in the flat. 'Me and Mattie are just going,' he spluttered, 'There'll be no more trouble Mister.' He grabbed a velvet collared jacket, took a final gulp from the jar then made for the door. A girl in her twenties was lying sleeping on a threadbare wartime utility couch, her dressing gown lying open at the top to reveal her left breast which caused Robertson to avert his eyes then stand with his back to her until the situation was under control. The man with the wine bottle grabbed some coins from a table as he made towards the hall despite the woman in the silver dressing gown screeching to stop him from taking them. One of the men shouted from the hall just before the door slammed. 'And you two can forget the dancing next Friday!'

'I'm Katie, and the lassie on the couch is my friend Rena,'

silver dressing gown announced just as the girl on the couch started to stir.

'Wake up, Rena, we've got a visitor!'

Rena rubbed her eyes and adjusted her dressing gown to cover herself up, sitting upright and lighting a cigarette without speaking a word.

'On your own, constable?' Katie asked, smiling through rouge-smudged teeth at the tall, awkward young policeman.

'Yes, I was going to the box along the road when a woman in the next close told me there was a lot of noise coming from here.'

Revived by several rapid drafts of nicotine, Rena became talkative. 'Auld Isa's always doing that. It was just those two arseholes arguing about something, but they're gone now. Listen, if you go and get your partner, we could carry on with the party!'

'Don't listen to her,' Katie interjected, taking over the interrogation. 'How long have you been at Oxford Street and what's your name?'

'Eh, Robertson, Police Constable Robertson.'

'Your first name's "Police Constable" then?' Katie and Rena looked at each other and sniggered, Rena choking and coughing to clear her smoke-filled lungs, before completing the joke.

'Was that what you were christened then, *Police Constable*? No other middle names then?' The women were laughing and coughing, revelling in their visitor's discomfort.

Robertson knew he needed to get out. These two were what his beat partner Morison would call 'as wide as the Clyde'.

'Now that pair have gone, I'll get back to the beat,' he announced, trying to regain lost authority.

Katie moved to the door, blocking his exit.

'No, wait, stay a bit longer just in case they come back.

Sure they sometimes do that, Rena?'

'Aye that's right,' Rena said sarcastically, 'they often do that when they've not got what they've come for. Here, Police Constable Robertson, has anyone ever told you you're the double of Clark Gable?'

Robertson was genuinely puzzled.

'Clark Gable?' he repeated.

The pair looked at each other before Rena asked 'Clark Gable. Don't tell me you don't know who he is? Where are *you* from?'

Realising Robertson was genuine, Katie came to his defence. 'Leave him alone!' Glaring at Rena, she added, 'Isn't it time you were across the landing?'

Annoyed, Rena stubbed the cigarette out into an ashtray full of red tipped fag ends. 'Oh, I get it. I'll get my stuff and go so you two can be alone.'

Panicking, Robertson pushed by Katie and went into the hall. She followed him and asked if he wanted a drink.

'No thanks, I don't drink alcohol,' he announced sternly.

'You know, I've never met anyone who doesn't drink! What time does your shift finish?'

'Why?'

'I'd like you to look back in again just to make sure me and my son are okay. Will you do that for me? Please?' she said imploringly.

That there was a child somewhere in the flat surprised and disturbed Robertson. But then, that's how these people lived. The unsanctified masses. 'I'll get someone to check on you later,' he said in his best official voice.She was insistent. 'No, I want *you* to come back. How long have you been in the Gorbals did you say?'

'Coming up for four years.'

'And are you on night shift all this week?'

Robertson had no idea why he felt the need to answer her probing questions. Maybe it was simply a matter of being honest.

'Till Friday. Why do you want to know?'

She tried to sound alluring.

'If I just happen to be looking out for you and you just happen to be passing any night around midnight ...' her rasping, nicotine-edged voice diminished into what she imagined was a seductive, come-and-get-me finale.

'Okay, will do,' he mumbled, now saying anything to get away.

'Bye, *Police Constable* Robertson' she called mockingly as he quickly made his way down the stairs. She closed the door and went back into the front room as Rena was tidying up, having changed into her day clothes.

'Sit down. Let's have another drink,' Katie decided.

'Oh, now he's gone you want me to stay?' Rena asked in sham surprise.

Katie wasn't listening.

'He's a bit of alright, isn't he? What age do you think he is?' she asked distractedly.

'About 30? A bit thick though! "Who's Clark Gable!" Where's he been?'

Katie considered the answer. 'Not thick, just ... well – different,' she concluded.

As ever, Rena was more pragmatic.

'I suppose you'll be needing to call the polis again soon?' She knew what her friend and neighbour was like when it came to men – dogged in pursuit then a doormat after the quarry had been bagged. So far, every single one of them had been bad news, yet Katie persisted, banking all on the one after this one being her saviour.

'I've checked. He's night shift all next week!' she announced knowingly. The women smiled at each other, Katie dreaming of her would-be uniformed protector and Rena to cover up her concern for her impulsive friend.

Police Constable Robertson's life was about to change

dramatically.

Katie Murphy's was on borrowed time.

Robertson strode off along the cracked and uneven pavement, deep in thought and seemingly unaware of the few persons still out at that time of the morning. He had never met any woman so forward in her manner and so obvious in her attraction towards him. It felt exciting. He began singing in his head to banish evil thoughts about what she might have been wearing underneath that lurid silver dressing gown. *Yield not to temptation. For yielding is sin. Each victory will help you. Some other to win.*

Once home at the end of his shift, he read from the book of Proverbs before he washed and went to bed just after his wife had taken the kids to school. The message was clear. *Wisdom will save you from the adulterous woman, from the wayward woman with her seductive words who has left the partner of her youth and ignored the covenant she made before God. Surely her house leads down to death and her paths to the spirits of the dead. None who go to her return or attain the paths of life. Thus, you will walk in the ways of the good and keep to the paths of the righteous. For the upright will live in the land and the blameless will remain in it; but the wicked will be cut off from the land and the unfaithful will be torn from it.*

My son, attend unto my wisdom and bow thine ear to my understanding that thou mayest regard discretion and that thy lips may keep knowledge. For the lips of a strange woman drop as an honeycomb and her mouth is smoother than oil; but her end is bitter as wormwood, sharp as a two-edged sword. Her feet go down to death, her steps take hold on hell. Lest thou shouldest ponder the path of life, her ways are moveable, that thou canst not know them. Hear me now therefore, O ye children, and depart not from the words of my mouth. Remove thy way far from her and come not nigh the door of her house.

Chapter 4

Theirs had been a wartime marriage, 22-year-old Janice marrying 25-year-old James in her hometown in the Scottish Borders in May 1942. The groom, from Riddell Street in Clydebank just north of the Glasgow boundary, had known the bride through family connections and he eventually proposed to the strict Congregationalist with the green eyes and honey blonde hair although she was not Brethren.

'Family connections' in their case meant first cousins.

At first, they stayed with Alison – James's mother in Radnor Park, Clydebank, then, when he joined the City of Glasgow Police, they moved to their own house in Glasgow's Southside, where their two children were born.

1940s Britain demanded self-interest take second place to the common good from its citizens. The state owned everyone, and life was simpler. There was good and there was evil and evil deserved to die and James, like most people, was wholeheartedly in agreement with the spirit of the time ghost, the covert agent of national survival in the worst of times.

Right from the start of married life, James made his views clear. There was little or no point in trying to understand or empathise with women as the Lord had placed them here to procreate, mostly, it had to be said, producing lost little souls eternally doomed from birth. One night on honeymoon after a brisk, wholesome walk, he explained that notions such as displays of public or private emotion or romance were worthless, Satanic distractions. Janice listened, then meekly accepted her dutiful role in the divine firmament. She was to expect comfort in routine domestic chores alone and that there would be few gestures of affection by him on the journey. She listened attentively as her new husband explained God's

16

Great Plan to her. But she wasn't as innocent and trusting as he imagined. Just as her mother had told her, she already knew that men's best laid plans and lofty pronouncements were sometimes just a cover for whatever they could get away with. It was reasonable for 'good' women to cook, clean, bear children then look after them and in return, the 'good' man would hand over an unopened pay packet at the end of the week, further details to be worked out between individual couples. In that respect, the Robertson household fitted nicely into what was socially acceptable.

Woman 1: See her next door's gone and walked into a cupboard door again! That's the second black eye she's had this month!

Woman 2: Aye, but she'd start a fight in an empty house, she would! Oh, and that man of hers is too scared to open his own pay packet before handing it over!

Indeed, Robertson went beyond basic requirements and treated his family well – if in a limited, benevolent despot kind of way; wholly in keeping with the times. The little ladies needn't know what goes on out there. Seven years of married routine later and the day after Robertson met Katie Murphy, he reasoned God was indeed testing him. He always knew he was special in His eyes and would one day be of use to the Almighty, so what harm in finding himself in Nicholson Street around midnight as the Sabbath ticked its way into the start of a new working week?

He took to his bed and Janice kept the children quiet until seven that night when she woke him and brought him tea.

'Here's a cup of tea, James. The children have done their homework and are playing a guessing game they learned at school. It's called "Hangman".'

James sipped the tea, unsure if such a pastime was a worthy use of life's precious time.

'I was never allowed to do that. As you know, Mother was strict about me not playing games. I think I'll take the children to church next Sunday, it would be good for them.'

Janice was concerned. He seemed distant. 'Is something bothering you at work?'

'No. Nothing more than the usual drunken fights and stabbings. Mother would have been horrified at the state the world's in. Most of the people I have to deal with every day have no way of avoiding temptation the way *we* do, and they fall into all the evil traps we know to avoid. Some of the older officers call weekends the "three P's". Do you know what that stands for? The pub, the prison, and the pawn. Men and women go to the pub and drink until they can't walk, then the men end up in prison and the women have to pawn things to get to the end of the week so they can start it all over again. The Lord has been good to us, showing us what to do, and when I think about all the times when I was growing up when I wanted something and my parents said no, I realise now that self-indulgence leads to hell.'

Janice left her husband alone in the bedroom, satisfied he believed he had chosen the true path, the path of righteousness – and confident he was doing good work in an evil part of an iniquitous world.

He readied himself for another shift, washing and shaving before getting into his uniform, all the time imbued with joyful spirit. His thoughts went back to his parents' house in Clydebank, like his own, sparsely furnished with no trinkets such as ornaments or pictures on the walls. As Mother sat listening, he would read the Scriptures out loud to her.

'The Lord Jesus sayeth as to His Disciples "They are not of the world even as I am not of the world"'.

'What did Jesus mean when he said that, Mother?'

'That's a very good question, James. He was telling us that the world we presently live in is split between darkness and light and only true believers can go to Heaven. We need to interact with a wicked world and save others if they are worthy.'

'What happens to those people who can't go to Heaven? Do they go somewhere else?'

'Yes. Because they have chosen to follow Satan's unrighteous path, they are eternally damned. We are lucky because we have chosen to be together for ever by rejecting sin. But we have to be careful that we don't lose sight of God's will.'

'So, if you sin a lot, you don't get to live for ever?'

'No, He will always help you if you stray and seek his guidance, so never stop asking him for help.'

As he washed the razor free of foam, Robertson considered those words.

We all need to interact with a wicked world, but *if we stray, we can seek his guidance.*

Chapter 5

As his usual partner, Morison, was off that week, Robertson was paired with the experienced Macdonald, a Lewisman who had learned that the streets of the Gorbals were as dangerous as wartime service. The two of them had never worked together before but they both knew what to expect from each other from workplace rumours and gossip. Robertson had heard that Macdonald was a good man to have beside you when razor gangs were on the rampage or a tanked-up husband was teaching a defiant wife some harsh lessons in life. He knew when to move in to end it and, more importantly – how to do it, drawing his baton only when it was the right time. Macdonald, though, liked a drink, so Robertson decided to be wary of him, at least until he got to know him.

Macdonald knew that Robertson was likely to be cold and duty bound, mainly because of his religious upbringing. He also had a tendency to spout passages from the Bible when the opportunity presented itself, but only after he became comfortable in your company.

'Watch out for him moving in to try to save your soul,' Macdonald was told, 'But treat it as a sign he likes you. He might even want you to be there in Eternity with him – along with his family and a few well-chosen friends.'

It was another warm night as they walked from Oxford Street to start their shift on beat number eight of Glasgow City Police Southern Division. Being the senior man, Macdonald made the running and started the conversation, using the name Robertson was known as in the force.

'I have to say, Ronnie, you look like a good man to be in the trenches with! It should be a lot quieter tonight, what with all the money gone on drink.'

'Yes, hopefully less to do tonight. They tell me you were on the Atlantic convoys during the war. That must have been tough.'

Macdonald smiled before a well-worn phrase came from his lips. 'You know, it's a toss-up what's scarier – a convoy to Murmansk or a Saturday night in Cumberland Street!'

Robertson acknowledged the answer with a polite nod. He had expected Macdonald's stock response to be reserved for later in the night. 'So, you still have family in Lewis?'

'Plenty of cousins, and Mother's still on the go. She's one of those long-lived Hebrideans who says a blameless life leads to a long one.'

Robertson's interest was roused. 'My mother used to say the same. Does she attend church?'

'We all used to, but she's getting too old now so the minister visits her a lot.' Macdonald, in turn, thought Robertson had wasted little time in getting to religion. 'Not that she doesn't have her own point of view and is not afraid to voice it. You should have heard her cursing thon Churchill when my cousin and I were on the convoys! "Churchill?" she would say, "He's Joe Stalin's pet dog! One day Uncle Joe's doing his best to ruin Britain, but as soon as Hitler attacks him, he's Churchill's best pal! And you and your cousin are going to a watery grave because of these two!" You'll understand that being a member of the Free Church, mother had strong views about most things. She still has no idea I take a drink.' *There, I've told him I drink now, and he'll just have to accept it.*

Robertson relaxed. Here was someone like himself, still coming to terms with rules and strictures from childhood. 'Were you ever banned from eating at the same table as your parents? My father did that to me a couple of times to prove how unworthy I had become.'

'No, that's a new one on me, Ronnie. Mother made us sing a Gaelic psalm before eating the food the Good Lord put on our table. Never banned though. Your church sounds worse than us Wee Frees. What were the woman's beliefs then?'

'I was brought up in the Plymouth Brethren.'

Macdonald knew he was treading on privately consecrated ground but, as it belonged to both of them, he saw the conversation through. 'Well, good luck to you, Ronnie. Sometimes it's tough being Free Presbyterian but I'm not for changing now, that's for sure. It's part of me for life. There were Brethren in the next village to mine and they seemed like decent folk, but all that stuff about the end of the world being nigh and the coming millennium was all a bit much for us. Mind you, they made us feel like non-believers what with their never reading books apart from the Gospel and them having no ministers.' He paused and looked up at Robertson. 'I hope I haven't offended you?'

Robertson shook his head. 'No, if anything I know what you're saying. As you said, once the faith gets you, it's hard to live without it in your life.'

'And have you managed to do that? I mean, can you live within the boundaries of your faith and still do a job like this?'

'So far, yes, but it does test you. I'm sure you've found the same.'

The pair had crossed Pollokshaws Road onto Cavendish Street when a boy of about ten ran towards them. He was wearing shorts, plastic sandals and a hand-me-down knitted red jumper with holes in it. He wiped mucus onto its sleeve as he spoke.

'You two! A woman in Nicholson Street gave me tuppence to find you. She needs you to get rid of somebody from her house.'

Macdonald asked the address and the boy said it was Mrs Murphy from number 139. Robertson felt a curious surge inside. She wanted him. She was Temptation. To

Macdonald's surprise, Robertson grabbed the boy's jumper and pulled him towards him, nearly lifting him off his feet.

'Look here, did she give you money to find *us* or was it any policeman she wanted?' he demanded.

The boy was startled. 'She never said. No, she said something about a polis that looked like a Clark Gable or something, but I don't know who he is.'

After Robertson let the boy go, the youngster ran a safe distance then shouted *bastards!* As he accelerated into Salisbury Street and towards Nicholson Street itself. After what Robertson had done, Macdonald became wary. What made him take hold of the boy's jumper when all he was doing was passing on a message?

'If you don't mind me asking, Ronnie, do you know the woman he's talking about?'

Robertson told him the story of what had happened the night before. He suggested it would be better that Macdonald go and see her himself. He was agreeable. 'Sure, I'll go and see what the trouble is. Just you wait at the close.'

There were no lights on in any of the houses at 139 and the gas mantle in the close was out. Macdonald got his torch out and made his way upstairs as Robertson walked up and down outside to avoid the stink of urine in the close. Isa appeared with her pillow to take in any drama to come, the noise of her window opening causing Robertson to briefly look up without acknowledging her. Macdonald was not long in coming back down the stairs. Rather than let Isa hear what was going on, Robertson made his way to the mouth of the close, stench and all, when he heard the heavy tread of his colleague's boots coming down the stairs.

'There's nothing wrong. She's on her own and done up like Jean Harlow, all made up and in a dressing gown. She's even got a Hollywood cigarette holder! But she was expecting someone else ...'

Robertson's blushes were masked by the darkness. 'Well,

it wasn't me. I was there last night and chucked out two men she wanted rid of . . . when I left, she was fine. And her friend from next door was with her,' he added defensively.

Macdonald suspected he knew what was going on. 'It doesn't matter to me, Ronnie. Funny things go on here and we're . . .' He stopped mid-sentence, deciding not to complete it by saying 'all men of the world' as his colleague obviously wasn't. Nevertheless, he could still make his point. 'Do *you* think you look like Clark Gable?'

Robertson sighed. 'She said that last night. I've never seen any films, and I have no idea who that is!'

Macdonald quickly realised Robertson was genuine. 'The only way out of this is for you to go up there and face her. Hiding's not going to work in this place. She says she has something to tell you and refused to say anything to me. Go on – get it over with and I'll wait here and chat to Isa who's trying hard to listen to our every word anyway.'

Robertson was gone for over 25 minutes. When he emerged from the close, he was perspiring and silent. Macdonald waited until they got to the police box at Cumberland Street before saying anything.

'Seems you had a lot to talk about after all!'

The attempt at humour did not go down well. 'Jezebel! The woman's a harlot!' Robertson ranted as Macdonald opened the police box up and lit the thermos stove under the whistling kettle.

Almost exactly one year later, Chief Inspector Dougall called Macdonald in. He wanted to know why he had applied for and been granted a transfer out of Southern Division and whether it was anything to do with working with Constable Robertson. By that time, of course, there had been some unforeseeable events in Dougall's division.

Chapter 6

Robertson had eventually settled in to beat number eight whatever shift he was on. Dayshift, he would get to know the shopkeepers who had trouble with shoplifters, backshift the publicans who had trouble with drunks, and nightshift the wives who had trouble with husbands. The number of uncollared dogs of all kinds was a constant menace and he soon became known as someone who had a way with strays, having some unknown power over them by the way he approached and calmed them. With his engineering background, he also had a reputation for diagnosing and curing the vagaries of the CID Humber Super Snipe which sometimes was reluctant to start or spluttered and coughed when it did. 'Get Big Ronnie to have a look at it' became a byword around the station if the police mechanic was busy elsewhere.

Big Ronnie. 'James' at home and 'Big Ronnie' at work. Janice hadn't heard his work name until she met another police wife one day who mentioned it. She explained that it had come about because there were two James Robertson's in Southern Division both based at Oxford Street. The other James Robertson had 15 years' service and no middle name, whereas Janice's man had only been on the beat for a year when she heard the reason for the nickname. He had never told her about it. Janice thought using his workname might lighten his mood after one busy nightshift when he arrived home at eight in the morning. For some reason though, he had reacted badly, and she never used it again, learning he was James the husband, James the father, James the Brother and 'Ronnie' at work. Two separate persons, it seemed, in one well-built frame.

Having been called out to an attempted break-in at the synagogue in South Portland Street, he got to know the caretaker Shimon, changed to Simon. He was a Russian Jew who had fled from the Czar's repressive regime in the Pale of Settlement and, to the policeman's surprise, they immediately got on well together. Although intrigued by the Israelites of the Old Testament, up until then he'd tried to avoid their descendants. After meeting Simon, though, he often called in when on day shift to check all was well. Over a cup of stewed tea, the white bearded old man would recall the pogroms and the poverty he had come from, always ending *you might not know it Ronnie, but you are lucky indeed to be from here,* in a thick Yiddish accent. Robertson used to question the truth of that, citing the obvious, grinding treadmill of despair all around them, but Simon's pragmatic optimism usually won the day.

'That, my friend, depends on what you're used to. Give people a proper chance and most of them will be hardworking and true,' something that Robertson had difficulty accepting. Experience, though, had taught him that many who lived there could be surprisingly cheerful and doggedly defensive about their much- criticised community.

Even so, most of them were *doomed to damnation.*

The pair almost fell out when one day when Simon jokingly suggested he should convert to Judaism, Robertson reacting bad-temperedly and accusing him of overstepping the mark.

'You know little of my life! I have a good faithful wife, a dutiful son and an obedient daughter. God is in all our lives and those who do not follow the True Path are the ones who must despair for their souls!'

Simon quickly apologised, pointing out he was not being serious, the remark being prompted by the news that the Goldsteins were looking to marry off their daughter Pearl to someone in the Jewish community.

'I was trying to be funny, Ronnie, please do not take offence. You see, like many others, Goldstein came here from the East with nothing and borrowed money from friends to start up his clothing business. Now he's a rich man. He helped pay for this building and he started the Glasgow Hebrew Benevolent Loan Company to lend money to those who came here in rags, like we all did. All I was saying was you might have been the man for Pearl if you hadn't been a married gentile!' Despite the possibly demeaning description, Robertson calmed down, mindful that his own strong beliefs sprang from the same common source as those of the old caretaker.

In time, the Jews who found refuge in the Gorbals moved on. Some of them had paid to get to New York and initially thought that was where they were when they arrived, but stayed anyway. The infamous Glasgow Gorbals might be the one of the most deprived areas in Western Europe, but it was a safe haven compared to Warsaw, Kiev, Przemzysl or Odessa. There the Jewish population were tormented and murdered despite sending their sons and fathers to arms for the countries of their birth. How could these streets covered in dog shit and those back courts lurking with the polio virus, dysentery, and what else Jehovah only knows, be better than where they fled from? But they were. The death squad gangs in the Gorbals murdered each other, sometimes on flimsy religious excuse, but never Jews. Their hatred for each other based on animalistic, territorial rivalry at Gorbals Cross at closing time when businesspeople were asleep. The people of Abraham came with nothing and, with the determination that dreams can bring, made money and settled in the sort of houses they were once not welcome on the doorsteps of. For the rest of the Gorbals though, life's bitter cycle continued for those unable to leave.

That day, Robertson left the synagogue a dissatisfied man, worried he had committed the cardinal sin of envy. In times of spiritual doubt, his mind went back to a childhood empty of warmth. He remembered the day a boy from school asked him if he wanted to play football in the park. The next day the same friend brought a Meccano set to school and the teacher let the boys play with it for a while, as it was near the summer holidays. But when young James asked his mother if he could play football and get a Meccano set of his own, she became bafflingly angry.

'No! You are not allowed! Those things are for other children, not you.'

Thinking his mother would be impressed, he persisted. 'Please can I go to Freddie's? His family have a radio!'

Mother was resolute. She made her views clear. 'Crystal sets and music are traps to amuse the unrighteous. They will distract you from doing what we must all be doing when we are not working – worshipping God!'

And the time his father caught him reading a book from school, *Just William*, young James was banished from the dinner table to allow him time to reflect on misusing his time on Earth. It had been genuinely mystifying. How could Richmal Crompton's stories about a spirited 11-year-old boy and his gang of equally imaginative friends, the Outlaws, be anything other than innocent fun? Father had taken the book from him then flicked through some pages before quickly deciding on its palpable profanity, William Brown doing things like going to the pictures then re-enacting what he had seen as he made his way home. Until then, young Robertson had been assured his place in Heaven was guaranteed but after that he saw his father in a different, unexpectedly harsh light.

'James *Ronald* Robertson, you have been found wanting in practising the ways of the Lord,' he pronounced, 'and will now have to show you are willing to follow Him in the Path of Righteousness.' It was a scary prospect for a boy the same age as the youth in the seditious tales he was no longer allowed to read. Something in the way his father emphasised his middle name, *Ronald* – only used when being rebuked over a God-displeasing incident – made him think. Was father using his middle name only when he transgressed because *Ronald* was the reason he had done wrong and slipped from grace?

So, on leaving the Synagogue that day, Robertson began to have doubts. Not doubts about being one of the Elect but doubts about why some people – like the Goldsteins – should believe in their God yet be able to indulge themselves and live in the comfort and pleasure of heaven on *this* side of eternity, like the decadent Corinthians St Paul mentions in the Bible. Was the 23rd Psalm not sung by the Israelites as well, and did King David's words not mean something to them? Why should they have all they want in this life *and* in the next?

He could fix cars but could never afford to own one on a constable's wage; he could look at detached blonde sandstone houses in the west end and only imagine what it was like to live in them. He could look at tight-skirted women in the town centre and revel in Ungodly thoughts about the marble skin and firm breasts underneath their corsets. God had made them but did he have to make some of them so desirable? He decided he had clearly not yet rid himself of *Ronald's* malign effect. Worse, that was what they all called him now at work.

Meetings at the Gospel Hall sometimes helped. Whilst the men broke bread and talked, some would hint how they came near to straying from The True Path. Yet no one ever seemed to talk of leaving it, wandering off to explore what it was like to experience sin, even if only to be chastened by its very doing. Surely that would help quell the doubts he felt about not having the things others had? Some of the Brethren had cars and large, detached houses with neatly kept lawns surrounded by rose bushes and rhododendrons, yet nobody had said they could not enter Heaven. When Brother

Geoffrey and Sister Maureen fell in love, no one, not even their spouses, questioned their right to stay in the church. Even now, everyone saw how they looked at each other and some even spoke of seeing them out walking together and holding hands *after* the scandal came to light. *The Lord will understand if I stray. He wants me to do wrong because he knows I will not be fragile and open to temptation when I return to the fold. Sin a little and spite the Devil. Thumb your nose at him by sinning so badly then, when he thinks he has your soul, repent and return to the One True Path. Ignorance of sin is a sin itself and lust, not adultery, is a cardinal sin. God's vanguard need to commit transgressions so that Lucifer recoils from their courage.*

Ronald will be exposed for what he is – one of the noxious burden of the wicked in this world who must be indulged, then destroyed. Yes, I will be a stronger, better man when I come back from what I now know I have to do.

Chapter 7

And so, it was settled. What he was doing was the Saviour's work. Night after night and day after day, Isa the busybody got used to seeing him patrolling her very own little part of Nicholson Street, mostly by himself. To begin with, street urchins would run up to him with urgent news of dire deeds and dreadful happenings at number 139. He would react *just in case they were true*, he convinced himself, but the watchful old crone at the window smiled knowingly at each fleet-footed appearance. Every time he went, the more he reasoned it was providential, the Lord leading him there for a purpose, the householder always on her own with tea at the ready and her child with a neighbour.

In time, routine took over as it did with all beat cops. Tea at Katie's became a regular nightshift halt as much as dropping in on Simon the Israelite at South Portland Street or after hours at the Clock Bar in Bedford Street for tea not liquor. For Katie, it was instant attraction followed by curiosity and planning; for both, though, it was a challenge, Robertson's set by God Himself and hers by the cachet of snaring her own personal protector. Goodbye kisses, once unheard of, became expected, then part of a customary farewell after she had patiently half-listened to her strange visitor's homilies about the Saviour's plans for her soul, all the while plotting and planning the next cast of her rod, the next baiting of her trap.

Then it happened. The kiss lingered longer than before, her grip remained firm and they kissed again and again until the Lord signalled the time had come and it had to be done, an unclean wife at home unable to perform her solemn duty and another, whose taint had been purified, providentially provided by the Lord. *God promises to forgive us and cleanse us from all unrighteousness.* But this was His work, His Will on Earth and was so ordained.

It had never been like this before. 15 stone of grinding man on top of Katie brought pain and blood where bare floorboards wrought friction and splinters, climaxing in oaths spat into her neck and ear, 'Bathsheba! Bathsheba! God be abundant in Grace and mercy!'

Thus, the Lord tested me His Servant. Why, O Lord have you allowed me to stray from Your teachings? You know I have kept your commandments. Who is the more sinful – the tempter or the tempted? How then can I do this great wickedness and sin against God? And the Lord replied, saying no temptation has overtaken you except such as is common to man. But God was faithful and would not allow me to be tempted beyond what I was able and with that temptation He also made the way of escape that I might be able to bear it. Bear it I did and continued sinning with this abandoned woman, always awaiting the Lord's direction that His work and my toil on His behalf was done, but none came. These were not my own desires but the Lord's doing and verily did I seek the path of righteousness until the Lord sayeth that bravely facing fleshly lusts as I had done, confirmed I had confronted the Devil and thus had shewn my courage and faith in God's covenant. Does not the good book say – I have been crucified with Christ, it is no longer I who liveth but Christ liveth in me and the life which I now live in the flesh I live by faith in the Son of God who loved me and gave Himself for me?

At the next Sabbath meeting, the Brethren spoke with many voices on what constituted His word, until Brother Ernest and Brother Nathan's views prevailed, yet one contrary to the other. When did temptation become sin? Was the covenant made with God broken by simply looking at young women or was it breached only when fleshly lusts had been satisfied? And when fleshly lusts had been satisfied, then satisfied again, was that a greater sin or a sign that God had marked you out for deeper understanding of the holy doctrine? The Book of James says: *Blessed is the man who endures temptation, for when he has been approved, he will receive the crown of life which the Lord has promised to those who love him.*

Brother Ernest, always the loudest in prayer and most skilled in catechismal responses, was satisfied he had won the day. But there was force in what Brother Nathan said, that it depended on what 'endure' meant before the word 'temptation.' If it meant 'suffer' or 'tolerate' or 'withstand' or 'put up with', then there might be no clear beginning and no discernible end to whatever form the temptation might take.

Having been approved already as one of the Brethren, James – the one most in need of guidance – found comfort and help in those words, his sin being unbearable to the point of exquisite pleasure. And sin begets further sin.

Confess your sins and God will show you mercy. If your brother sins, rebuke him; if he repents, forgive him.

Chapter 8

The scene on Prospecthill Road was suspicious from the start. One of the first to attend was Police Constable Kevan, a traffic officer who had seen the results of many hit and run accidents before, and this one was different. Pedestrians sometimes misjudged the speed of traffic on the road and took chances, walking or running into the path of a tram or a trolley bus or a private car, their judgement shot by alcohol. Sometimes drivers forgot to switch their lights on at night and hit the brakes too late when someone absent-mindedly stepped out onto the road. Dark vulcanised tyre impressions on the tarmac would lead directly to bloody tissue mingled with glass, paint flecks and dried mud where the two collided.

Kevan cast an experienced eye over the road. Where was the point of impact? Where were the tyre marks that spoke of a driver's split-second frenzy to stop a hurtling mass of metal striking flesh, bone and blood? Instead, the signs were confusing. Kevan trod carefully round the crime scene, noting where everything was. Women's shoes at the side of the road, a white plastic handbag close to the centre and bloody tyre marks on *both* sides of the body told their own story. Somewhere in the city this lifeless corpse had begun the night brushing her hair, putting on bright, garish lipstick and choosing what to wear from a cheap and limited selection of well worn, tawdry outfits. How did she end up here dead on the asphalt? Her few possessions scattered around her, now ring-marked in chalk and soon to be eternally preserved in stark monochrome court production photographs that recorded what was left of a once cherished life coming to a bleak and vicious end.

His insistence that this was no accident did not endear Kevan's sergeant to his conclusion.

'So, if it's not a hit and run, what is it? You do realise the traffic enquiry boys will have to spend until first light taking measurements and noting the scene? They'll have to close the road.'

Kevan was firm. 'If it's not a hit and run, it's a murder. She's been run over then reversed over then maybe run over again. At least a couple of times if not more.'

A check of the handbag showed no money and no identification which, looking at the body, came as no surprise. She did not look the type who went to dine at *La Fourchette* in the Central Hotel then spend time sipping a post prandial cocktail on the terrace. Even so, finding no house keys was unexpected. She must live somewhere and wherever it was, she needed keys to get back in, unless it was one of those areas where there was no point in protecting nothing of value. Or did her husband knock her down then drive off with the keys in his pocket? If so, he had some questions to answer.

A few hours later, after Chief Inspector Dougall started dayshift at Oxford Street, DS Passmore updated him on the events of the night in Southern Division.

'Quietish night, compared to Friday and last Saturday. A serious assault in Ballater Street, near the Cross but after being stitched up at the Royal, the victim, one Joseph Kerr, says he fell and cut his face on the railings at the underground toilets.'

'Joey Kerr from Eglinton Street? Is he back out? One-time leader of the Cumbie. You'd think Joey would know how dangerous these railings can be!'

Dougall's sarcasm was borne of cynicism. If the likes of Kerr didn't care, why should they?

'I know – especially when he must have fallen three times, according to the admissions nurse. Then there's the road traffic death of a 40-year-old woman in Prospecthill Road. She's probably Katie Murphy from Nicholson Street.

Her neighbour, Rena Hughes was looking after her two young boys after the deceased woman said she was going out for ten minutes last night, but she never came back so Hughes shouted out the window to a passer-by to call the police.'

'*Probably* a woman from Nicholson Street?'

'Yes, she was on her own with two kids but Rena Hughes described her right down to the pattern of the second hand dress and the plastic shoes. The post-mortem's likely to be this afternoon across the road at the City Morgue.'

'Who's going to identify the body? Are there no relatives?'

'She's got a sister somewhere in Lanarkshire but no luck in tracing her so far. The neighbour doesn't want to, but if pushed she said she could identify the body.'

Dougall tapped a pipe out into a thin metal waste bucket as he pondered the situation.

'I want you to take a policewoman with you and go and see this Rena character. Sounds like she might know something about her neighbour's private life. The kids' father – or fathers – will need to explain where they were when she was killed, particularly if he has a car.'

Passmore was back with an hour.

'Well, Rena's not going to win the Katie Boyle award for Hostess of the Year. She's pretty upset. She told us we couldn't get in without a warrant! Would you believe it? Her friend and neighbour's just been done in and she's effing and blinding at us because we're the polis! Who does she think is going to catch the killer, then? The local gangs? The Cumbie? People like her puzzle me. Some of our beat boys spent years fighting Hitler and neds call them fascists!'

Dougall understood. 'She's probably in shock, after all, she's just spent the night looking after two kids who are never going to see their mother again. Give her a bit of time to cool off then go back round and tell her she's helping Katie if she identifies her, otherwise it's fingerprints and that will take a day or two to organise.'

'So, the deceased is on file?'

'Nothing major. A couple of shopliftings when she was a teenager and a breach of the peace a few years ago when her man and her fell out.'

Dougall had called it right. Rena had calmed down when Passmore went back and Katie's two boys, one only three months old, had been taken away by two policewomen for temporary fostering, pending a longer term decision. It did look like Katie's sister had enough to do without taking on another two, her having five of her own and all under twelve.

Rena was more subdued when she and her police escort went to identify the body. Passmore pushed open the incongruously decorated stained glass windowed doors of the City Morgue and they entered the arcane world of enthusiastic pathologists, recently deceased cadavers and the smell of formalin. The sound of a mortuary attendant's cheery whistling was heard to stop abruptly as a trolley covered in green canvas with patches of dark brown staining nosed its way into a small annexe where the three stood, Rena nervously clawing at a cheap yellow metal ring on her right hand. Passmore went into one of the better rehearsed spiels that cops in Southern Division were used to making.

'Miss Hughes, this gentleman is going to pull the cover back so that you can see the face of the person who is underneath. He will hold the cover back as long as you require so that you tell us if you recognise the deceased person. If you are able to identify them, I will ask you that person's name. Take as long or as little time as you need.'

Blood-matted, peroxide-lightened hair emerged as the cover was slowly lowered, followed by darker roots interspersed with grey and white. A purple tinged depression in the bony structure of her right forehead gave way to a fixed grimace underneath, the jaw seemingly locked open in a toothless, derisive grin. Rena muttered 'Jesus God!' and nodded several times. 'That's her! That's Katie! The poor soul! Oh my God, what has he done?'

Chapter 9

Dougall still thought Rena was the key to solving why her friend and neighbour had been mown down a couple of miles from her dirty and cramped one bedroom flat. Katie's last words to her had suggested she was not going to be away for long and it was not like her to take such advantage of Rena's necessarily limited stock of goodwill. Both women had had to adjust to sinking deeper and deeper into debt, dirt and despair, but they had the comfort of being able to rely on each other when they really had to; the limit was reached when it came to either of them foregoing a brief chance of fleeting fun rather than look after another's sickly child. That worked both ways and Rena knew she could call a few favours in when Katie came home that night.

Except she hadn't.

Dougall waited until the known facts pointed in a certain direction before he could confront her and make her confess what she clearly knew about the dead woman's private life, and therefore tie up the enquiry's loose ends. 'What has *he* done?' needed explaining, but what Dougall was getting so far was not what he had expected.

He knew that Morison and Robertson had attended a call to a disturbance in Cavendish Street the night before, after which Morison had spent some time on his own. Dougall also knew that Sgt Mair had spotted Morison out walking on beat number eight by himself as he, Sgt Mair, drove back from the potential crime scene locus at Prospecthill Road. At the time, nothing was made of Morison being on his own. There could have been many reasons for him and Robertson to have split up, depending on what a busy shift threw at them. It was part of the job, stopping off at pubs after hours and calling in at Dixon Blazes for tea on a cold night. At first, Morison was reluctant to say where Robertson – known in police parlance as his 'neighbour' – had gone to. It did seem odd, however, that Robertson had logged details of what had apparently happened in Prospecthill Road when it was a couple of miles south of his beat *and* furnished a description of the driver that no one else had been given. How would Robertson know about the man's Burberry coat or where he headed after the incident or even that the car was a ten-horsepower dark blue Austin? Presumably, he had been given the information by a member of the public whose details he had not noted and so could not be traced again.

Dougall's thoughts were interrupted when Passmore knocked on the door then came into his office.

'Morison and Robertson are on nightshift again tonight, but something funny's going on – Morison's not gone home yet. He's back in and wants to speak to you.'

A grubby, tired looking Morison was led into the room by Passmore, who also sat down after Dougall gestured him to do so. Morison had clearly not been home since finishing his shift several hours before, his uniform rumpled and stained and his face unshaven. A smell of drink wafted across the desk and Dougall thought he must have spent most of that morning in the back room of one of the Gorbals' many pubs, 'one on every corner' and well over a hundred at the last count.

Dougall spoke first.

'Don't you think you should be going for some rest? You're meant to be back out again tonight.'

Morison's expression was pained. If drink had given him any relief from what he was about to say, it was temporary and maybe even made it all the more difficult.

'I thought I should maybe speak to you before I went home for a sleep rather than wait till later when you might not be on.' He was finding it difficult to get to the point and Dougall recognised that.

'Alright, we've done some digging and know you and Ronnie went to a breach in Cavendish Street. What happened after you two went there? Before you answer, I should also say that Sgt Mair later saw you on your own in Cumberland Street as he made his way back from a road traffic incident in Prospecthill Road.'

Morison knew it was time to tell the truth. He exhaled a long, powerful sigh which wafted an alcoholic aroma across the room.

'The fact is boss – I went to the rammy in Cavendish Street myself.'

Realising that Morison was on the verge of possibly saying something significant, Dougall kept silent to allow him to carry on speaking. Passmore started noting Morison's words.

'Ronnie asked me to cover for him in the early hours …' Morison muttered.

Dougall filled the void in an effort to encourage Morison to say what he had to say. 'So what? These things happen. I've done that myself on nightshift in the past.'

Morison took a deep breath. 'I covered for him because he really was going to see a blonde, and I'm not sure if it's the same one that was run over. He's been seeing her for a while but I never asked the details.'

Dougall was taken aback by the unwelcome news. For Morison to suspect a neighbour was one thing, but for him to implicate someone he had worked beside in a serious crime was unheard of. The men who pounded the beat together in a place like the south side built up close relationships, often to the exclusion of the truth and the ears of their CID colleagues. They had to be able to rely on each other in tight spots, and a code of silence had developed between neighbours that would only be breached in certain critical circumstances. A road traffic accident would *not* meet the test, but murder would.

Dougall knew he had to press on, fearing what he might hear next.

'Where did Robertson get the information from – about the man in the Burberry coat? Were you with him when he filled in the log in the Cumberland Street box?'

'No. He did that himself. And you do know he's got a black Austin? You've been in it.'

'I knew that. I asked him how he could afford it and he said he couldn't but that a friend had loaned him it.' Dougall was still hopeful they were all making a terrible mistake. 'And why make up the car involved was an Austin?'

Having gone as far as his duty made him, Morison wanted out. 'You'll have to ask him about all that. Listen, I need to go home now for a couple of hours if I'm on again tonight.' Having done the right thing, Morison now had to weigh up the consequences of what he had started.

After Morison left, Dougall made a decision. Passmore was to go to speak to Rena once again whilst he was going to visit Robertson at his house in the Penilee district of the city.

Passmore wasn't convinced Dougall was doing the right thing.

'What's the point in that? If he says anything that incriminates himself you know as well as I do that it couldn't be used against him in court. He's now a suspect and you can't just barge in and ask him questions. What if he admits running her over – it's vital information that can't be used.'

Dougall knew all that was true. 'You're right of course. Two reasons I have to do this, I suppose. Firstly, he's been here for nearly five years and we can't just ignore that. I owe him the courtesy of a meeting. What if there's another explanation? I hope to god there is.'

'And the second reason?'

'The second reason is that I'll know as soon as I look at him if he's done this.'

Dougall drove to Robertson's house anxiously hoping his

suspicions were wrong. Robertson had gone home after his shift finished and had gone to bed beside his wife, who had then got up and made breakfast for the children. She had then taken them out to the local park to feed the ducks. At five o'clock, Robertson heard the door being knocked but he ignored it. Dougall knew better than most callers that a cop on nightshift could easily ignore the door for the sake of an extra ten or even five minutes sleep, so he persisted. Not only that, if Robertson was in, he must be sleeping, not just sleeping but hopefully in a righteous, conscience-free slumber.

Robertson went to the door, thinking his wife had forgotten her keys and was stunned to see Dougall on the doorstep.

One look at Robertson dashed Dougall's hopes. This was not the tall, poker-stanced cop he knew. His words were uncertain as he saw the haunted, preoccupied look in the constable's eyes.

'Sorry to bother you at home when you're on nightshift, but I need to speak to you.'

Robertson stood, not reacting to Dougall's words and cutting an almost comic figure in tight, ill-fitting pyjamas. Dougall realised he had to take control of this and changed his tone to that of superior officer. He even used his proper Christian name.

'James, let me in so we can talk.'

Robertson automatically stood aside, his head downwards, his features unresponsive. For a second, Dougall wondered if he should follow Passmore's advice and leave well alone but he went in, even if just to make sure there was no other explanation.

Robertson sat down without speaking as Dougall stood beside a table with four chairs round it. There was little else in the room apart from a display cabinet with a wedding photograph on it showing a smiling bride and groom, their arms linked in innocent, blameless wedlock. Dougall noticed the glass was cracked.

'You must be wondering what I'm doing here,' Dougall began, Robertson staring silently at the floor beside him. 'Unless you've already guessed, in which case, I better just leave.' Robertson reacted by lowering his face and staring at the floor. With his hands wrapped around his ears, he slowly shook his head from side to side in total silence. Dougall made his way back to the front door, his heart sinking as he opened it in time to see Robertson's family coming up the short garden path, the children's smiles contrasting with their mother's startled expression.

'Mr Dougall, what brings you here?' she asked mechanically, already conscious that it had to be something important involving her husband. Both of them were keenly aware how awkward their chance meeting was.

'I needed to speak to James about an urgent enquiry before he came on duty.' It wasn't quite a lie but was preferable to saying *Ronnie probably murdered the mother of his third child.*

She ushered the children into the house. 'And was he able to help you?' she asked pointedly.

Driving back to Oxford Street, Dougall cursed himself for ever going to the house. Not because of any legal intricacies that might have arisen, but because he now knew for sure that Robertson was somehow responsible for ending the life of one the desperate Gorbals residents on his beat and in his care, so to speak; no matter, the law had to be seen to be done even if it went against an instinct to protect one of his own officers.

All he and the rest of the CID had to do was to prove it beyond a reasonable doubt – beyond a doubt based on reason – when reason itself yelled "why"? Why become entangled with a woman with nothing but pain to offer when you have a wife and kids with everything to look forward to? Why stray when everything you were brought up to believe in makes it clear that it's wrong to do so?

Or was it *because* of that? Does having strict moral standards hammered into you as a child make it all the more appealing to lead yourself astray in later life?

Chapter 10

Before Dougall got back to Oxford Street, Passmore compared notes with the recently promoted DC Blake. Blake was yet to adapt to Dougall's sometimes brusque manner and was worried the increase in his salary would be temporary should he be more outspoken than he ought to be. That Dougall looked like a slightly smaller version of James Robertson Justice only added to the aura surrounding his nickname in Glasgow CID – Tiger. Somewhat nervously, he asked Passmore if what he had heard around the station was true.

'Has Chief Inspector Dougall actually gone to PC Robertson's house to speak to him about that woman getting run down?'

'Yes, he told me he was going to do it.' Passmore still thought the move ill-judged.

'Why? If he's a suspect, he should stay away and arrange a proper interview, policeman or not.'

'I know. Trouble is, Dougall's got a soft spot for him and doesn't really want to believe it. After all, none of us do. Ronnie's a man for the rules, well he was until now.'

Not wanting to pry too much but keen to know what the evidence was against their colleague, Blake probed a little further. 'Being a man for the rules sometimes works the other way. I mean, just because somebody professes a belief in their God, doesn't mean they are immune to wrongdoing, does it?'

'No, that's one thing I've learned over the last fifteen years, everybody's capable of committing a crime of some sort. My old aunt lives in a fishing village in the north and my dad used to say she was so worried about sinning, she sometimes swore just to ease the tension! Can you imagine her sitting at home blaspheming quietly behind closed curtains in case the neighbours heard?'

'True. If you worry about being bitten by a Gorbals Alsatian, it's more likely to happen, I suppose. Where does it end? You'll be telling me next that Billy Graham's a part-time safe blower! So, what is there new against Robertson now?'

'Hopefully, the pal Rena's beginning to open up now it's dawned on her how serious all this is. Dougall doesn't know this bit yet, but she reckons her friend Katie was having a long-term affair with a beat cop. She claims she never saw him because he wanted it kept quiet.'

Blake was rightly sceptical. 'That's just nonsense! She never saw him? In this place? Rubbish! These people practically live on top of each other and she never saw him on the stairs or outside the close?'

'Hang on, it gets worse. She says that Katie's baby – the second boy – was fathered by him too.'

Blake whistled. 'Who'd have thought Robertson was up to that? Have you ever met Janice, his wife? Like we thought he was, she's a devout, practising Christian who lives a blameless life. Rarely wears make-up because Robertson's church banned it, I heard, but she never needs to. Lovely looking woman. They seemed that happy together.'

Passmore agreed but weighed up the facts.

'She must have known what Robertson was doing. Every wife does when her man's cheating on her. Anyway, you can almost see how this one goes. Gets himself involved with another woman, she gets pregnant and wants money from him after the baby's born, otherwise it's goodbye to his marriage, happy or not. Begs the question though, does having an affair mean the marriage was unhappy? I'm not sure it does. Just means he couldn't keep it in his trousers, like lots of men.'

Blake noticed Dougall parking the CID Hillman Minx outside. 'Here's the boss. Tell me, how did he get the stupid nickname – "Tiger"? Was he a war hero or something?'

Passmore laughed and shook his head. 'No, nothing like that. It goes back to when he was made up to Sergeant about fifteen years ago and some of the beat boys reckoned his attitude changed. It's "Tiger" because they said he became ferocious when he got his stripes!'

Blake stifled a laugh before Dougall appeared.

Dougall was pensive when he came in. He closed the door over before he spoke to the other two about his ill-judged visit to the Robertson house.

'He said nothing but it was as good as a confession. Couldn't look me in the eye and just sat rocking back and forward with his head buried in his hands. The whole thing was really painful, then his wife and kids came in all smiles and happy – well the kids were. I felt sick when she showed up.'

'He's due on nightshift tonight. What are you going to do about it? And what about Morison?' Passmore asked.

Dougall scratched his forehead like he always did when he was thinking. 'I've just heard the Rena woman's beginning to open up a bit. We need more to charge him, so Morison's coming in at five to show us where Robertson keeps the car. He thinks it's in a garage in Surrey Street so we'll get a warrant from the Sheriff before we go any further. The whole thing stinks like a two-shot suicide.'

Chapter 11

Passmore and Blake shooed the local kids away from outside the lockup. A group of boys were playing football with an old leather bladder which had seen better days, and that had deflated to about two thirds of its size. After going to the trouble of creating their own version of the national stadium, the street footballers gave the policemen the usual abuse as they were moved back to a safe distance. The brick wall around the lockup doors had a shakily painted white goal post on it although the doors themselves were securely locked with two hasps with large Chubb padlocks. Such security measures obviously made the place more interesting for some of the local residents, one of whom had tried hacksawing his way through one of them before giving up. Some girls playing skipping in the street stopped their game when they saw the four police officers. Two of them in uniform were paying attention to the garage door and, as happened in the area, went to tell parents and neighbours that something was going on. A small crowd soon began to gather to watch and pass comment. Some asked if this was to do with 'Katie getting murdered' and feelings were running high just as another uniformed officer appeared with a set of keys. Out of earshot of the assembled onlookers, he explained that Tiger had been given them by Robertson who had appeared early at Oxford Street. He possibly had no intention of going on shift and had turned up unshaven and in civilian clothes. He was seen to speak briefly to Morison as he came into the office and had asked for Dougall at the front desk. Before Dougall could caution him, Robertson had handed the lockup keys to him along with an ignition key for the heavy 16-horsepower Austin colleagues had become used to seeing him drive in recent weeks. After what had happened, the same colleagues discovered Robertson's explanation for unexpectedly becoming a car owner varied from it belonging to a friend who had taken a job abroad to a generous brother, who had never been mentioned before, giving him permanent use of it. No one had queried either explanation and Dougall himself had been given a lift in it after a long gruelling day shift had ended a few weeks before.

After he had been given the car keys, Dougall postponed Robertson's interview until he heard from Passmore about any incriminating evidence that might come from the vehicle. In the corner of his mind, he still held out hope that there could be an explanation other than what was plainly unfolding. Maybe there was no forensic link to the car and Robertson was just being weird, in a passive Plymouth Brethren kind of way, scourging himself for being part of this wicked world and infuriatingly offering no defence until it could be shown he actually had nothing to do with the woman's death. Or maybe not.

Back at the lockup, Passmore instructed one of the uniformed cops to stand outside the doors to keep the inquisitive pack of locals at bay whilst he and the others examined the car by torchlight.

As soon as Passmore opened the doors, the torchlights criss-crossed onto the registration plate, DYS 570. He made a note to check if it had been reported stolen. Then there was the smell, or smells. That usual aroma of worn leather from the seats was tinged with another, sweeter whiff baked together in the unusually warm night air, the particular odour of blood and dead, rotting tissue. The other uniformed officer got down on the ground as if about to perform ill-timed press-ups and shone his torch underneath as Passmore examined the body work for signs of a collision. Nothing, apart from a small dent on the rear bumper.

'Sir! There's blood on the concrete floor!' The cop on the

ground had an urgent note in his voice.

Passmore wondered if it was possible. Brake fluid maybe? Driving all the way from Prospecthill Road to here must surely have rid the undercarriage of dripping blood and mangled human flesh. He shone his flashlight onto the tread of the tyres. Both offside were almost bald but the rear nearside had fringes of rubber which held trapped, darkened patches. He went round to where the man on the ground was still commenting from his vantage point. 'And there's stuff sticking to the driveshaft that doesn't look right …'

Passmore got down on his knees and shone his torch underneath, lighting up small round blotches on the ground, too light-coloured to be oil and too dark and viscous to be brake fluid.

'And the exhaust pipe's broken at the silencer,' the man on the ground said, Blake adding, 'And it's tied up with rope. A real rushed job if ever I saw one!'

It was decision time for Passmore. 'Ok, time this was moved to the garages across the road. Nobody touch anything. You three stay here so that none of the locals come calling for souvenirs and we'll get the flatbed lorry over as soon as we can.'

Waiting to hear from Passmore, Dougall met Macdonald by arrangement in the corridor and took him into his office. Assuring him it would be off the record, he asked him about the short time he had been on foot patrol with Robertson the year before. At first, Macdonald was cagey in his replies, intuitively protecting his one-time partner. After Dougall told him there was probably enough evidence for Robertson to go through the Sheriff Court on petition for murder, regardless of what Macdonald did or didn't tell him, Macdonald unwound and opened up a bit more. He conceded he had been on beat number eight with Robertson in July the year before when one of the local kids had run up to them and told them they were needed at an address in Nicholson Street. It had been Robertson's idea that Macdonald go to the house himself, which he had done. He described what had happened after that.

'I could tell by the woman's face she was disappointed it was me and not him who had turned up. He's a fine big fellow. I know it's the dead woman we are talking about but it was obvious she was the one who was interested in *him*. If anything, he was frightened of her. The poor woman was wearing a silver dressing gown and silver high heels and doing her best to look like Rita Hayworth or something, God bless her. She said she wouldn't talk to me and insisted I leave and that he come up instead. After I went back down the stairs and told him, he went up to see her. He was away for about half an hour and was flushed and had his collar loosened when he came back. Whether he was or not, he sounded angry and I think he called her a "Jezebel". By the time we got to the box in Cumberland Street for our tea break, he had calmed down again.'

Dougall got to the point. 'Why did you transfer out to Northern? Did you see this coming?'

At first, Macdonald was unsure how to reply. 'No, I didn't see anything like this coming but there were two reasons for moving. Above all, it suited me after my wife got a teaching job in the north of the city. After that, I suppose I also did *not* want to be around to see what I thought might happen to him.'

The reply puzzled Dougall. It was a strange thing to say considering she had been murdered and Robertson was soon to be the accused man. 'You mean Robertson? What was going to happen to *him*?' Macdonald nodded.

'I was worried that she would eat him for breakfast, knowing the sort he was. What with the Brethren background and all that, he was not what you might call streetwise despite having the service he had by that time. I would hate to think what might happen to some of the young fellas I know from Lewis if they ended up in a place like this. I didn't want to see what was about to happen to Robertson and his family, so a move out made sense.'

'Did he talk to you about her?'

'No, apart from a few quotations from the Scriptures, he never confided in me. Mind you, it doesn't take much to imagine what went on between them whilst I was chatting to old Isa in the street outside. I heard Isa passed away last year. Pity. She would have been a superb witness. Never missed a thing, *hinging* at that window of hers. Would have given you dates, times and phases of the moon if you asked her.'

Dougall's phone rang and he took the call, Macdonald sitting the whole time waiting to leave. Having nodded and gestured with his thumb towards the door as if seeking permission to go, he remained seated after Dougall waved him to stay where he was. Call finished, Dougall had one further question.

'Tell me honestly, is Robertson one of those religious fanatics that everyone avoids? I've always liked the man and found him trustworthy. Up until now, that is.'

'I think his beliefs are deeply held, but now wonder if he's the proverbial iceberg and there's a lot about him we just don't know about. Did you hear about what happened when he found out about Lambie's spoof on *Holy Willie's Prayer*?'

Dougall confessed he hadn't.

'It was just a bit of fun. You know Lambie does the round of all the Burns Suppers, well he did one called *Holy Ronnie's Prayer* which Robertson got wind of. To begin with, he had never read it, nor for that matter any of the Ayrshire Bard's work. He seemed to quite enjoy it right up to a couple of verses that somebody had underlined, you know the ones:
"But yet, o Lord, confess I must,

At times I'm fashed wi' fleshly lust
And sometimes too in worldly trust,
Vile self gets in
But Thou remembers we are dust
Defiled wi' sin
O Lord yestreen, Thou kens, wi' Meg
Thy pardon I sincerely beg
May it never be a livin' plague
To my dishonour
And I'll never lift a lawless leg
Again upon her.'''

As a survivor of countless boozy Burns inspired nights,
Macdonald was able to recite both verses with ease, before
getting to the point – how Robertson had reacted.

'Well, does he not tear it up and storm out before Lambie
had a chance to explain it was just a bit of fun or to apologise?
He really had no idea the big fella would be like that.'

In the meantime, Robertson had agreed to being
interviewed – not that he had much choice. At 33 years old
and having served in the City of Glasgow Police force for
nearly five years, the appeal court was unlikely to review
whatever he said at interview as unfairly obtained – he was
neither a teenager nor a vulnerable adult. Whilst Glasgow
juries sometimes enjoyed convicting policemen, there was
nothing tangible in his background or his answers that an
experienced counsel might present to their Lordships as solid
grounds of appeal. It would be left to the luck of the draw,
the vagaries of fortune, the ups and downs of life seen from
the dock of the North Court. *Now, if you were a plumber or
a caulker and not a policeman, the jury would be on your
side. You see, they don't like convicting of murder here. It's
often culpable homicide even when the evidence all points
one way to a downright, cold-hearted assassination.*

By the time the heavy old Austin had been moved and the

lockup secured against the locals, Robertson had given Dougall *some* of the story. Not enough to go anywhere near explaining why an overtly religious man, married with a seven-year-old girl and a four-year-old boy should mow down a 40-year-old single mother of two, then – to make certain she was dead, deliberately drive back over her lifeless body. This one had 'personal' stamped on it from the start.

The truth was, the suspect could never have told anyone the real reason for what he had done. Why he executed Katie Murphy would forever be a secret, a clandestine act not capable of rational explanation or logical description to outsiders – people like vindictive jurors jealous of his position in this world but, more importantly, unaware of his link to the next. *Unlike them, he already had his place in Heaven.*

Chapter 12

Not that there wasn't a secular account Robertson was able to give after being cautioned. True, he *had* told Morison he was 'going to see a blonde', that catch-all phrase used on many a night shift to cover many an indiscretion. Also true, he had left the car in a lock-up no one had been using, apart from him, and had fastened it securely against discovery. Apart from that, Dougall needed little else to make a case.

How many vehicles with minute fragments of human flesh and torn   fabric matching the dead woman's dress and body were likely to be on the road that morning, then hidden in a garage within a couple of miles of the accident scene? Linking Robertson to the car was complete and tying the dead woman to Robertson was in progress. So, with a heavy heart, Dougall arranged for someone he regarded up until then as one of his better officers to be locked up pending an appearance at the County Buildings in Ingram Street the next lawful day, the main charge being murder by motor car, other less serious charges to follow. A heavy heart because 138D had five years dedicated service, had two commendations – one for rescuing an elderly man from a fire in Surrey Street – was never late for his shift and never complained about working late. When Robertson joined the force in November 1945, one of Dougall's CID predecessors had summed it up. 'Those Brethren are a bunch of conchies but now the war's over, you can trust them completely. You see, they'll always do the right thing because they're not out to please or help anyone apart from God. He's their Chief Inspector, not me!'

As he always did, Robertson had reported for duty well before he was due to. His clockwork devotion to being punctual still applied, regardless of the unfolding tragedy and his part in it. Mainly because he was the sole topic of conversation, his arrival in the locker room silenced the others either coming off shift or waiting to go on duty, a fellow officer slipping away to let Passmore know that Robertson had turned up.

The interview had confirmed opportunity, handing the keys over and a cursory inspection had confirmed means and method. After seeing the car and the fleshy human debris mangled into its undercarriage, Dougall and Passmore sat in silence, reluctant to take the next unprecedented step of actually arresting one of their own. A murder suspect would be cuffed as a matter of course but it just didn't seem right here, like restraining a trusted friend. Everything they knew they had to do felt intuitively wrong. Eventually, Dougall sighed. 'Go and tell him to come and see me again.'

After Passmore left the room, Dougall suddenly yearned for retirement, still two years off, but now surprisingly appealing. He had never felt like that before and this had to be the nadir of a career filled with many low points borne of witnessing many inhumane and selfish crimes against weaker and more vulnerable victims. The elderly lady in Salisbury Street with no living relatives who had to pay 'protection money' to one of the young members of the Fulton clan sprang to mind.

Through the frosted glass door panel, he caught sight of the two figures approaching, Passmore leading the way. That Robertson had made no effort to change into his uniform was bad as it further pointed to a guilty conscience but good in another way. *Funny how practical things like not having to ask him to change out of his uniform mattered at a time like this. Can't have him charged with murder then have him change back into civvies. Anyway, there was something inherently improper about cautioning and charging a man wearing the outfit of law enforcement.*

Passmore moved a chair for Robertson to sit on, directly

facing Dougall across the paper-strewn desk. He stood to one side, awaiting Dougall's lead in these unparalleled circumstances. Robertson had trudged in behind the detective, then sat down without questioning the reason for his attendance. Once he saw Robertson's expression, Dougall had the same awful empty feeling he had experienced in Robertson's house earlier that day, but less so at interview where he wasn't as forthcoming as might have been expected. The man was guilty and he couldn't hide it.

Best to make this brief. 'James Ronald Robertson, I am arresting you for assaulting Miss Catherine Murphy aged 40 of 139 Nicholson Street, Gorbals, Glasgow on 28 July 1950 on Prospecthill Road, near Aikenhead Road Glasgow whereby you struck her and did drive a motor vehicle over her body there and you did murder her. You are not obliged to say anything but anything you do say will be noted and may be used in evidence.'

For several seconds, Robertson's dull, bloodshot eyes barely reacted. Then, as if emerging from a deep internal debate, he suddenly spoke in a soft, remote voice, answering, 'That, sir, is entirely wrong.' He might as well have been speaking in an unknown foreign language as the shock of the exercise had numbed Dougall's senses. At the time, he recorded the words without thinking about them, later concluding that Robertson's only hope was that it had all been a catastrophe caused by momentary carelessness and that the assumption he, the CID and the traffic officers had all arrived at was 'entirely wrong'.

As Robertson was led to the cells, Dougall felt a twinge of unprofessional sympathy and made a phone call on the prisoner's behalf. For such a tall, imposing figure and with years of experience in one of Europe's most deprived areas – post-war Berlin excepted – Robertson seemed helpless and unworldly, as if saying or doing something to his own advantage was beyond him. Godliness, in his case, meant guileless naivete when it came to defending himself. Dougall picked the receiver up and dialled Laurence Dowdall's office. He was told he was on a short holiday, but a message would be sent to him to consult with the incarcerated policeman as quickly as he could on his return to work. In the meantime, Robertson was in His Majesty's Prison, Barlinnie, with all the problems that brought for one of the hated opponents of most if not all of the inmates there. If convicted of capital murder, he might never be leaving its pitiless environs, his earthly remains forever rotting in an unmarked, unconsecrated, shallow ground-scrape outside D Hall after his spinal cord had been severed by judicial order.

That evening, Dowdall and his wife made their way arm in arm past reception in an old fashioned, rural Argyllshire hotel, having just finished dinner. On seeing them, the receptionist left her station behind the sold oak counter to intercept him, it being more respectful than calling after him.

'Sorry to bother you. A telephone call came for you during dinner and I decided to wait until you finished before letting you know.'

The couple looked at each other, knowing that business was intruding on pleasure. Even so, no point in not being polite. 'That's very thoughtful of you, my dear.' Dowdall said. 'I take it it's to do with work? Tonight, the dining room is infinitely more important than the office.'

'Yes, your secretary called asking you to phone her first thing tomorrow, so I knew it was safe to let you finish dinner.'

Dowdall turned to his wife. 'Looks like we may have to curtail our stay. Perhaps a nightcap is in order before retiring?'

Mrs Dowdall shrugged her shoulders. 'Why not? Just this afternoon I was thinking how lucky we've been with no distractions so far.'

The receptionist suggested they take a seat in the tiny but

grandly named Cocktail Bar and she would arrange for the waiter to attend and take their order.

No one else was there as they took their seats in large leather armchairs opposite each other, a small glass topped table between them. Typical of a Victorian legacy common to hotels of that kind, the ubiquitous stag's heads and 'Monarch of the Glen' type paintings embellished the walls. It had been another warm day but a wood-stacked hearth crackled and radiated an aroma of smouldering pine and birch into an empty room, just in case guests were tempted to come in.

A fresh-faced young waiter in a red formal jacket approached respectfully, a silver tray in hand and a notebook open and ready. Returning with a sherry and a gin and tonic, the young man self-consciously announced the drinks were on the house, causing Dowdall to protest.

'No, there's no need to ...'

The waiter insisted. 'My mother owns the hotel – she says it's a token of appreciation for your custom and she hopes you'll enjoy them. Anyway, it's not every day I get to meet someone I've read about in the newspapers.'

'I hope it's all good,' Dowdall said as he raised a glass to his lips.

The waiter seemed to relax and it looked as if he was readying himself to pull up a third chair to block their exit from the cramped corner before he could complete what he had to say.

'It's all good. There's something fascinating about the law. The criminal law I mean.' It sounded as if the young man had been biding his time to tell his story.

'You know I had a notion to go into law myself but went into engineering instead. Very dull by comparison, I'm sure.'

He paused. Sensing the young man's discomfort, Mrs Dowdall recognised his need to speak and did not want to appear standoffish and rude, so kept the flow going. 'Even so, I hope you have more free time than Larry gets. We get little time away as it is and we might have to cut this break short as well by the sound of it.'

It sounded like a green light to continue and, unable to stop himself, the waiter eagerly pulled a chair over and sat on the edge as he continued with his yarn. The Dowdall's exchanged glances. *He's going to be here for a while.*

'I'm pally with a couple of law students. One of them went to see a jury trial you were in and he'll be envious when I tell him you stayed here and I met you!' After a pause, he added 'Both of you,' lest the wife took offence.

She hadn't, and was used to strangers coming up to them, mostly to pass on messages of goodwill, although some came up with the usual hackneyed observations, complaining about defence lawyers still being able to sleep at night after defending guilty people. So far though, this young man appeared fairly normal, so she joined in.

'Now don't say things like that to Larry or he'll have an even bigger head than the one he came here with!'

The waiter finally got to the point of his continued presence. 'Before I go, can I tell you what my friend said when he came back from court that day?'

This might now go either way. Dowdall hesitated before agreeing he could continue with the story.

'He told me that when the Deputy Fuhrer, Rudolf Hess, parachuted from his Messerschmitt into Eaglesham near Glasgow in 1941, the local with the pitchfork told him to get his hands up then asked him who he was. Hess did as he was told and when he said his name, the farmer asked him why he had fled Nazi Germany. Hess said because he had done some bad things and by that time, the farmer thought it was some kind of trick so he shouted at him "So what the hell do you want here?" and Hess shouts back "Get me Dowdall!"'

Always polite, the Dowdalls smiled and laughed enough to convince the waiter he had come up with something original, something neither of them had heard before.

When Dowdall first heard the tale in or around 1948, he painstakingly explained he was serving in the Royal Navy during the war, before he realised the Hess story was made up and meant to be flattering, the apparent purpose of the Deputy Fuhrer's bewildering excursion being to seek sound legal advice from someone with a burgeoning reputation. Dowdall had not recognised himself when he first heard the joke but since its telling was at least a weekly occurrence, he tended to smile and nod knowingly as if to say *Well done for passing that on!*

Satisfied, the waiter left to tidy up behind the bar as the Dowdalls sipped their drinks. 'If you had a penny for every time you heard that …' Mrs Dowdall started to say, her husband finishing it by adding, 'I would have no need ever to work again! But, I have to be honest – I would miss it.'

'I could see you now,' she began. 'Wearing your court blacks addressing a jury, saying, "Ladies and Gentlemen, I appear for and represent Herr Hess. What you must not do is pre-judge the case against him simply on the basis he was once the Deputy Fuhrer of the notorious Third Reich!"'

'Who knows? I might even get paid for that, unlike most of the cases I get!'

She finished her sherry then sat deep in thought. 'I wonder what's so urgent they have to contact you here? Do you think it might be that tragic accident where that poor woman was run down by the policeman on duty? You would think he might not be locked up when it looks like he was doing his job. Some of my Bridge friends were wondering why he's in prison.'

'If you're right and it is that case the call was about, at this stage your Bridge friends know more about it than I do.'

During the trial, Dowdall recalled how he had ended that conversation. 'If experience is anything to go by, there has to be much more to this story than meets the eye', words he later mused were intense with understatement.

Chapter 13

A stale, desolate aroma of sweat hung over the overcrowded prison. It first assailed the nostrils about fifty yards from the gate then grew in strength at the first checkpoint, burrowing deep into people's hair, clothes, and memory. For inmates, it had already begun in the confines of the ancient black Bedford bus that transported the remanded prisoners from court, its ventilation restricted to four small apertures at the front and a small, constantly turning windmill on the roof. Like a dutiful bee returning to its hive, the bus returned to Barlinnie twice a day, taking some to court and bringing some back from it, continually entering and re-entering the odour zone and incrementally adding another layer to the pungent aroma on each visit.

At first Robertson looked out of place in the bus as he sat erect and upright amongst other less robust prisoners, who soon came to recognise him for who he was. Extra escorts had been deployed to ensure no trouble on route, but it soon became clear that solitary confinement was the only solution for the renegade cop. By the time the bus braked to a juddering halt, Robertson had slumped into a round shouldered posture like the rest of them, resting his forehead on the palms of his hands. Taken out first, his prison admission was processed separately in a corridor outside the assistant governor's office, his belongings bagged and recorded by a stiff capped prison officer who had volunteered for the assignment. He spoke in a loud officious tone.

'From now on, Robertson, you are a number and not a name. You are no longer a member of society, a police constable, a husband, or a father, but will answer to the number you are about to be assigned. Do you understand?' he shouted.

Robertson nodded apathetically.

'I can't hear you, speak up!'

Robertson managed a softly spoken, 'Yes.'

'Alright. Firstly, your property. Can you confirm you had the following in your possession when you were arrested, viz: one ten-shilling note, one florin and one sixpenny piece. Next, two collar studs, one front and one rear. One silver coloured wristwatch of indeterminate make with a worn leather strap and one (Yale) house key for the use of.' Robertson stared vacantly into space. 'Speak up, man!' the martinet warder shouted.

'Yes.'

'Ok. From now on, you must obey all commands given by myself or by my colleagues at all times. For your own safety, you are being placed in a cell by yourself in a unit attached to 'C' Hall. This is chiefly on account of your recent service as a police officer, but there is another reason for that that you might not be aware of. The victim of the so-called accident you were involved in recently – you might understand that in this establishment we have no choice but to go along with the fiction that all remand prisoners are innocent until proven otherwise, laughable as that may seem – is related to another of our current guests. He has expressed a desire to make your acquaintance, as it were, should the opportunity arise. I'm sure I do not have to spell out what sort of greeting he has in mind for you, given your time in keeping order in the city streets where you no doubt picked up many a pearl of wisdom which can now be usefully employed in the course of your sojourn in this establishment. Regrettably, I have to oversee an intake of drunks, pimps, and thieves that have just arrived at booking so I'll bid you good afternoon and leave you with my colleague, officer Duncan here, who will no doubt administer to your every need.'

At that, the guard spun sharply on his heel and marched off at a brisk pace. Duncan smiled as he explained his colleague's behaviour. 'Buchanan was a sergeant in the Scots Guards. He treats everyone like that. He wishes the war was still on, so he could do something heroic. You see, he missed almost all the action on account of having broken his ankle and although he hates shirkers, he despises conscientious objectors even more and thinks you were one because of your beliefs. Don't worry, most of the rest of us are nearly normal.'

Robertson looked at him through lifeless eyes as he spoke, nodding listlessly when he finished.

Duncan recognised how difficult this had to be for him, so sped up.

'Change into these clothes and give me the ones you are wearing just now – I'll add them to your property. You'll get them back when you leave here.'

He curtailed the usual introductory lecture at that point when it occurred to him that in a few months' time, the prisoner standing before him might be re-dressing himself in these very clothes for a last short walk across the landing to the gallows. Better to end the discourse on a more upbeat note.

'Being a remand prisoner, you have certain privileges including having relatives bring you clothing to wear for your court appearance and lodging money on your behalf. That's one of our standard jokes in here every time one of our guests gets his court clothes handed in. Stop me if you've heard it. What do you call a man from the Gorbals wearing a suit?'

Robertson was unresponsive, as if Duncan was talking to himself. He soldiered on. 'The accused! Get it? The accused. Because he's wearing a suit! It's like he walks about Cumberland Street all the time dressed like that! Like a jury's going to fall for him being a respectable man the rest of the time!'

Duncan finally gave up. It was as though Robertson

was somewhere else. Having changed and had his clothes added to his list of possessions, Robertson was taken to his cell and the door was locked. He hardly noticed the single mattress covered with a coarse woollen blanket which had faint brown staining at the top. There was also a piss-pot in the corner, sitting amidst discolouring stains on the greyish concrete floor.

Robertson sat on the wafer-thin mattress, the trestle creaking under his weight, before he knelt on the floor, his hands clasped together in supplication on top of the tarnished bed cover. To an inquisitive warder, their latest inmate appeared to be praying for the Lord's guidance and support, but his appeal to the higher authority had to wait until more earthly, practical considerations were taken care of first.

How will Janice deal with this? Will she even try to visit me here after she hears the full truth? Will she bring me clothes or put some money into my possessions? I hope not. She should not hear any of this. After all, she hasn't really spoken much after she found out I gave her crabs ...

Chapter 14

After the meeting got off to a hesitant start, Dowdall was surprised at how intense the client had suddenly and unexpectedly become. To begin with, Robertson looked and acted disinterestedly, as if his lawyer was talking about somebody else, a stranger in another place. Yet, as soon as Dowdall mentioned Janice, Robertson burst into an animated insistence that neither she nor the children 'should be dragged into this,' was how he'd put it.

Dowdall was sitting in the grubby interview room. The heavy glass doors at both entrances were in case of trouble which could be seen and extinguished quickly by the warders. When he arrived at reception that morning, he knew nothing of the case, even less than his wife's bridge partners, so had a blank sheet for precognition in front of him. As ever, he began doodling on the page (a habit that led to counsel nicknaming him 'Doodles') before the client had been brought into the room. After that, he carefully noted the client's details in dark fountain pen ink, as told to him. The trusted routine was not just to get the client used to talking but was also designed to allow the other person time to survey him, like turning side-on to a dog to show no threat. The prisoner was led in by a warder shorter than him by a full head, which gave the pair a faintly comic appearance. He undid the adjoining handcuffs using a small key from several hanging together on a large metal ring and the prisoner sat down on the bare grey metal seat without speaking. The warder about turned and left without saying anything, but stood outside pretending not to stare in. Dowdall nodded and bid his client good morning and Robertson repeated the words back. First impressions. Dowdall was well dressed and confident, Robertson attired in a brown prison corduroy suit, the seams of which strained to keep up with the pressure his shoulders applied. Dowdall noted his pencil moustache and gleaming white teeth, and subconsciously began considering the pros and cons of his situation. The female jurors will think him attractive – the male jurors might resent him for it, but all that was secondary to his occupation. Being a policeman was unlikely to find much favour with a mixture of citizens from some of the deprived areas in the city. Even so, Robertson looked like he could have been the model for the kilted figure on the memorial to the 51st Highland Division, forever gazing eastwards towards Beaumont-Hamel on the Somme – said to be a favourite of the now thankfully deceased Adolf Hitler, and accordingly not damaged in the Nazi occupation.

Dowdall spoke first.

'I am just going to introduce myself today and take some details, not many, then I'll return in two days to speak to you again.'

Robertson signalled his understanding and approval by nodding his head. Being only vaguely aware of his client's beliefs, Dowdall thought him unusually self-possessed in the circumstances. He decided he had been writing long enough and it was time to get started.

'What I do know is that the petition against you contains three charges and what I have to say is that at this stage, these might just be holding charges and the charges on the indictment might be different. The first charge alleges theft by housebreaking, the second theft of a motor car and of course the third is an allegation of the murder of Katie Murphy on 27 or 28 July this year in Prospecthill Road in Glasgow. It's probably better you do not give me full instructions this morning about how you intend to plead to those charges, although you can give me an outline of your position if you wish.'

Robertson spoke at length for the first time. 'I can tell you about the car. I noticed the Austin parked near where I live some time in the middle of June. It was on waste ground and when I checked our records, I saw it had been reported stolen in May from the city centre. I'm not proud of this, but before I joined the force, I was an engineer and I love tinkering with engines and as I could never afford to buy a car on my pay, I decided to keep it.'

Dowdall tried not to look surprised. From the little he knew of this man's background, theft definitely did not feature. Of course, he was also a serving policeman seemingly committed to upholding the rule of law.

Robertson continued. 'I cleaned the points and carburettor and soon got the engine running. It must have been around then that I thought it would be doing no harm if I kept it for a while, before the rightful owner got it back you understand.'

Expecting him to disapprove, Robertson hesitated but Dowdall continued writing, even pretending to do so when he had finished taking notes in order to underline the first rule of statement taking – remain stoical and never express censure. It's the only way to build trust.

Robertson waited a few seconds then carried on. 'Because it was a common model, I decided to put false plates on it, so it started life as CVD 350 and became DYS 570. I got hold of a blank registration book and filled it in so that everything looked legitimate, and I told my wife Janice and everyone at Oxford Street that it belonged to a friend who was working abroad and he had given me a loan of it. They all accepted that explanation and I even started giving other officers lifts home in it and no one suspected it was stolen.'

As Dowdall noted the words Robertson was speaking, his impression of the client began to alter from that of upright citizen to a man who must have initially strayed from the straight and narrow. He had clearly chosen to stay there for longer than he intended, like a first-time gambler betting more than he meant to. His instructions about the murder of Miss Murphy were now likely to be unexpectedly challenging.

'And did you know Katie Murphy?'

Robertson's brow darkened. 'Her? I did know her. We became friends. She lived on my beat – you get to know people quite well when you're walking the streets every day.'

No hint of anything beyond social familiarity. Better to leave it at that today.

'And what about the night of 27th into 28th July? Did you drive the car that night?'

Without hesitation, Robertson flashed a film star smile, gleaming teeth framed by a dark, well-groomed pencil of hair and a strong masculine jaw. 'That was the night I had decided enough was enough and it was time to get rid of the Austin before my luck ran out. My shift began at 11 that night and I told my neighbour, PC Morison, I was "going to see a blonde". That's just police lingo for taking time away from the beat. It's really nothing to do with seeing a woman, you understand. We've done that sort of thing before, me covering for him and him covering for me. Anyway, I cleaned the car down, rubbing away all the fingerprints from the steering wheel and behind the rear-view mirror and cleaning out the ashtrays. I left the plates on but wiped them down as well. After all that though, just as I started it up and drove off, the exhaust broke and it started making a noise like a Spitfire. I had to pull over to stop drawing attention to it and to tie it up with some rope that was in the boot. It was a muggy night and by the time I got it fixed, it was about 1 o'clock in the morning and I had to get back to my beat, so I had run out of time to dump it somewhere. Obviously, I had to tell Morison about the exhaust needing repaired because of the time it had taken and because I was covered in muck and sweat.'

One step at a time. He knew the dead woman. They'd even become friends. Best not to probe too deep at this stage.

As Dowdall completed his notes in the prison car park at the end of the interview, certain uncomfortable thoughts kept resurfacing. Robertson accepted he was in possession of the car at the time of the accident, if that was what it was; the lawyer had heard that the car could be forensically linked to the incident. The exhaust just happened to fracture that very night for no apparent reason and perhaps above all else, why did he not start the night by replacing the false plates with the originals if he was genuinely going to dispose of the Austin?

Then there was the arrogance of it all. Who was going to question a uniformed cop's ownership of a car? Why should they? The way he told it, it sounded perfectly natural for him to be driving about in it.

For that matter, who was going to doubt a serving policeman's account of what happened to Katie Murphy, whenever Dowdall deemed it the right time to ask him about it? The whole car business sounded too glib, seeing it on waste ground then putting false plates on it and just happening to getting hold of a blank logbook for it. If a regular client came up with that kind of stuff, you would automatically assume it was invented nonsense. Was this client any different from the desperate street tea leaves who always try but always fail to justify the reasons for their actions? Maybe he was worse. At least the desperate types can sometimes plead grinding poverty and dire need.

Surely *some* part of his account had to be true? Was there more than just bluster to this hugely deceptive man? *And we haven't even got round to discussing the serious stuff yet.* Time to go and see Tiger.

Chapter 15

Dougall and Dowdall had got to know each other through their appearances in court. Despite often having divergent interests in the outcome of cases, the pair had grown to trust each other and Dowdall had gained the Chief Inspector's trust to the extent he knew he would be able to get the inside track from him, particularly in a case involving a serving police officer.

Serving officer or not, the CID had done a thorough job in collating the evidence against his new client. Courtesy of Morison, it had not escaped the reporting officer's notice that Robertson had put himself in possession of the car when the vehicle had seemingly crushed the last vestiges of life from the dead woman. Once the underside of the car had been submitted for forensic examination, it had been carried out with rare precision by Professor Glaister. He had recruited an unlucky female police employee of a similar build to the deceased to lie under the car in various positions until he was satisfied that the coming together of flesh and blood and motorised metal could not have been accidental. Very unlikely at least. The examination took five days, much to some behind the scenes amusement of several of the shapely woman's male colleagues who made up laddish suggestions to each other as to where and how she should lie next and what poses she should adopt. As the accused was one of their colleagues, such ribaldry was put down to gallows humour – or perhaps more accurately, pre-gallows humour, by senior officers. By the end of the process, Glaister was *almost* able to confirm that the small dent on the nearside of the rear bumper of the car could not account for it mistakenly striking the unfortunate woman's legs. Almost but not quite, something which would be vigorously tested at the trial by the accused man's senior counsel.

Dougall had more to tell Dowdall. 'We got a warrant for his house and found blank vehicle logbooks that had been stolen from a garage in the course of a break-in, and it's in Robertson's beat. The serial numbers run consecutively and the one he completed is part of the same batch. We also found out he used his own unofficial rubber cosh which was in his jacket pocket.'

Dowdall weighed it up. 'So, he's stolen the car, made out a new logbook for it and there's no doubt the Austin was the one that ran her over. Where does the cosh come in?'

Dougall sounded pained. 'I've known that man for nearly five years now and for all of that time I would have trusted him with all I hold dear. He's stable, mature and trustworthy. At least he was up until now. If the Chief Constable had asked me to name a model officer, I would have said 138D, James Ronald Robertson. Good background, nice family, lovely wife and regular as clockwork. It's like he's gone mad or something. You know he's Brethren, don't you?'

'Yes. I don't know much about them though.'

'Fundamentalists. Meant to devote their free time to studying God's word and seeking his guidance, not knocking off cars and breaking into garages to steal logbooks, let alone having affairs then murdering their mistresses.'

Dowdall was surprised to hear Dougall talking like that, sounding as if he was off duty and chatting to a fellow CID man.

'What makes you so sure it was murder?'

Dougall sighed. 'I sincerely wish it wasn't. This is like a nightmare for me. The professor spent days going over this time and again. I asked him to, I suppose hoping there was another explanation, but murder by motor car it most definitely is, the first, I'm told, in this city. At post-mortem, she had a bruise on her temple which looks like it must have been caused *before* she died. They can tell these things, you know. In any event, one scenario is that she gets out the car holding her shoes for some reason – maybe he's told her to get out and she's not had time to put them back on. To think I got a lift from him and he's probably been using the car as a knocking shop!' Dougall's frustration had temporarily got the better of him. He coughed then regained control. 'Anyway, as I was saying, she gets out then he gets out and hits her on the temple with the cosh before dragging her onto the road where he lays her down before running her over to try to make it look like an accident.'

Dowdall never made any false outward pretence of being the cold hearted, consummate 'professional' like some of his colleagues who were apparently able to make light of clients' misfortunes. Like getting hanged.

It wasn't in his nature. His heart sank when he heard this latest development. It sounded so clinical.

'And you'll obviously know the full background. There's little doubt that the baby is his. She refused to tell welfare who the father was but she told her pal Rena it was a Glasgow policeman, and he's the one who's been seeing her since last year!'

Dowdall must have looked crestfallen. Dougall shook his head. 'I know, I know. Things were bad enough for her, but without the welfare payments, she must have really struggled. Sadly, it's a short step to imagining what happened after that. He's told her not to mention his name and she's agreed. Then she's asked him for money, and he's been unable to give her much – or maybe even any. He's on six pounds a week!'

Dowdall finished the likely chain of events for him. 'I see. He can't let her go public, so the next step's murder. I'll go and speak to him again tomorrow. Hopefully sense will prevail and he'll come clean about what was really going on with Miss Murphy, otherwise this is not going to end well. Anything else?'

Dougall sighed. He sat quietly for a moment before

he spoke, painfully sifting through any more relevant information that might be of use in somehow ending this tragic turn of events.

'Yes, her sister picked him out at a parade as the man Katie had been seeing. Oh, and for what it's worth, his reply to the murder charge was 'That, sir, is entirely wrong'. I can tell you that because I cautioned and charged him myself and the 'sir' is me. I made a point of it, maybe because he'd been fooling me and the rest of us for so long. Do you know he's told at least three different versions of who gave him the car? Brother, brother-in-law, uncle, you name it!'

Dowdall knew he was getting this information from the top and could see how understandably frustrated Dougall was. His latest client had surprised everyone by revealing just how different his true character was from the devout, reliable, and honest exterior of the man he had successfully impersonated for so many years; a real Eugene Chantrelle, a mind split in two with Jekyll at the North Pole flaunting his virtue to the world and Hyde lurking at the South, plotting evil and immoral crimes for his own gratification. 'The man's a puzzle,' he offered, his thoughts summarised into a neat, end of meeting precis.

He rose to leave. Dougall stood up and walked outside with him, changing the subject to holidays and family to try to clear his mind, but just as Dowdall began to walk away following a farewell handshake, Dougall called out. 'Laurence!' Dowdall stopped and turned round. 'Yes?'

'I forgot to tell you something. Janice Robertson came in to see me. She's a credit to any man. That just adds to the mystery. No tears, no hysterics, I'm sure she knew what was going on but the last thing she needs is for him to be acting like a sulking child.'

'In what way?'

'She's been up to try to visit him a few times but he's refusing to see her. It's bad enough he's in the Bar-L, but what it must be like for someone like Janice to have to go there and mingle with the friends and families of the hard-boiled neds in this city, I can't imagine. Maybe you could make him agree to see her?'

Dowdall took his glasses off and rubbed his eyes as he did in moments of stress. 'We both know that's not how it works. I do as he instructs me to and the best I can do in return is advise or suggest things that might help. I'll see what I can do, though.'

After Dowdall left Oxford Street, Dougall tried to immerse himself in paperwork but found he was too preoccupied with reconciling the impression of Robertson once fixed in his mind with the deeply unpleasant image of the cheating, violent thief that had now emerged. It had been like a sudden tidal wave on a placid summer beach, devastating all in its path without warning.

As the man's boss, Dougall felt somehow responsible. Once the inevitable enquiry began – the one that councillors were already calling for – were there any markers, any warning signs that he had overlooked? His accusers would have the benefit of hindsight and would be able to sound off about a homicidal maniac masquerading as a representative of law enforcement walking the streets at night, no doubt looking for further victims, should he have escaped detection. The jumped-up, publicity-loving baillies and local representatives in George Square were going to relish it.

Unless of course Dougall could go down the unlikely route of convincing the outside world that – short of going on beat patrol with his officers himself – he had to rely on both trust and track record to build up a picture of a man's character. Yet there had been few indicators that Robertson was anything other than steadfast. At work. Where it had happened. Damn!

He got hold of Robertson's personnel file and sat hunched

over his desk until his back ached but still couldn't find a key to unlock the puzzle. References from Singers, Rolls Royce and Beardmore's qualified him easily for his role in the City's new post war police force, a brave new world of freedom-loving citizens rightly basking in the afterglow of victory over fascism and safely going about their business in orderly fashion. Or so the fable ran.

Only two possible clues emerged. Tucked away on file was a confidential report by McAlinden, a now transferred former 'neighbour', who expressed concern that Robertson was increasingly and needlessly rough with cheeky kids. He had reported that Robertson often applied seriously painful sole-of-the-boot retribution to rear ends rather than the traditional token swipe that made little or no contact.

Then there was the time Robertson *went out of his way* to give Dougall a lift after work. Having casually made the offer as they passed each other in the corridor, Dougall recalled initially declining it as it would entail Robertson taking an inconvenient detour. Robertson, though, renewed the invitation just before his day shift ended. With less emphasis, Dougall had again demurred, this time on grounds of disruption to Robertson himself, Dougall likely to be working later than him. However, Robertson would not be put off and he insisted on remaining at work for an extra hour solely to fulfil the proposal. Not that this was questionable, as the constable used his time profitably, typing up low level crime reports until Dougall was ready to leave. Nor was there any evidence of him simply trying to ingratiate himself with a superior officer; such behaviour was often followed up with unwanted, tiresome invitations to social events such as weekend house visits, the hope presumably being that a reciprocal offer might be forthcoming, sparking off a regular chain of mutual family gatherings.

Dougall was confident that Robertson's proposal had no such basis. From what he knew about him, after hours recreation in his household revolved round discussions about the scriptures and few had had the privilege of meeting Janice.

It was when Dougall exited the vehicle, the lights from a car passing the other way captured a curious look on the driver's face, a fleeting, sly smile that, looking back, said *There! I've got you too! You're now part of all this because you took a lift in my stolen, disguised Austin 16!*

Chapter 16

Dowdall returned to the prison the following morning armed with the new, deadly facts he hadn't known before, that his client had chosen not to tell him. He felt some annoyance as Robertson *must* have known they were bound to emerge at some time. It was as if he thought he could brazen it out and the whole thing might go away, like a toddler who covers his eyes with his hands and genuinely believes the other person has disappeared.

It was now time for him to face reality.

Robertson appeared calm and unworried when the escort brought him through, casually smiling as they went through the same handcuff unlocking procedure. Once free of the cuffs, he sat down as the escort closed the door behind him. In contrast to their previous meeting, Dowdalls manner was direct.

'Good morning. Let me outline what I have discovered since we last spoke. You told me you were in possession of the car between 11p.m. and about one a.m.. I can now tell you that the prosecution has made the scientific link between the car and the deceased woman. There is no doubt that the car was the one that ran her over. It's better that you tell me the truth, or should I perhaps leave you now to let you think things over?'

Robertson was stunned. He sat in silence for a while as Dowdall arranged his papers and opened his briefcase, readying himself to leave. If need be.

Across the table, the other man crumpled. Resting his forehead on the grubby surface, he began to convulse, his powerful shoulders heaving up and down as he began making great sobbing howls. Dowdall moved his case onto the floor, waiting for his client to regain control of himself.

The sobbing though, transformed into a guttural wailing sound that then varied into a steady, repeated moan of "No, please God, no, this can't be happening to me!"

Hearing the commotion, the escort quickly appeared at the other side of the glass door. He unlocked it then peered in lest either the client or the lawyer was being attacked or that one of them was ill. Possibly thinking the latter, he let himself in and stood behind the prisoner, laying a hand on his back. Robertson sat up, wiping mucus onto a shirt sleeve, leaving an uneven green patch that straddled the corduroy lines of his jacket and sank into the spaces in between.

'Everything okay?' the escort asked unnecessarily. Dowdall nodded as he proffered a crisp cotton handkerchief to Robertson, who took it and started wiping his face before telling the warder he was fine. The escort left and Dowdall picked his briefcase up and opened it again, removing his fountain pen and the yellow precognition pad he had started to complete before the client had been brought in.

'Alright, shall we start again?'

Robertson took a deep breath, wiped his face again and agreed they should.

'Okay, this time I want you to tell me the truth. You are the only person who can say what happened. Will you do that?'

Robertson took a final face wipe before offering the hanky back. Dowdall gestured for him to keep it and Robertson began speaking as he pushed the sodden item into his prison trousers' pocket.

'Yes, I was there when it happened. Because I didn't want Morison to know that I intended getting rid of the car that night before the truth about it came out, I told him I was seeing a blonde. As I told you before, that just means doing something unofficial, that's all. I drove the Austin down Cumberland Street, along Pollokshaws Road and into Cavendish Street where I saw Katie Murphy standing at the corner. She came over and jumped into the car then asked me to do her a favour. I asked what it was and she said it was to run her to Neilston so she could look at a new house she was thinking of renting. I said I couldn't and she became all sulky. Her mood had changed from giggly to stroppy just like that. I drove her some of the way and we ended up in Prospecthill Road near Hampden Park and she then changed from wanting me to take her to Neilston to wanting me to take her to Rutherglen Road so she could visit her friend Agnes. I was fed up with her treating me like a taxi so I stopped the car and told her to get out so I could get back to my beat. I said if she wanted to act like a schoolgirl, she could walk home from there.'

Dowdall scribbled as the client spoke, sometimes using his own shorthand that only he and his secretary could understand. Questions could wait until the client had burned himself out.

Robertson was getting to the crucial part of the story. 'I told her the best I was prepared to do was to run her home from there, otherwise she would have to walk. But she was in a strange mood. She told me that if I made her walk home, she would sherrick me up and down Warwick Street.' Robertson paused to explain what that meant. 'Warwick Street is the old name for Nicholson Street, well part of it anyway. They changed its name because it had the worst reputation in the Gorbals. You know what "sherrick" means? It's not a word I knew until I worked in Southern Division – it means give somebody a bad name.'

Dowdall waved a hand to indicate he knew what it meant. No point in interrupting him to explain he knew most words used in polite company and everyone used in less gracious circles, such as Warwick Street as it once was.

Content he had cleared that up, Robertson carried on, seemingly glad to be unburdening the truth. 'I stopped the car and told her to get out. She refused and I leaned across her and opened the passenger side door, but she just sat there, so after we argued for a while, I was getting anxious about being absent from my beat and I shoved her shoulder to push her out. After that she stood on the pavement shouting that I was going to get a real showing up. I put the car in gear and drove off. After going about 300 yards, I had calmed down a bit and it occurred to me she might be frightened on her own on that stretch of road with nobody else about, so I put the car in reverse and backed it up quite rapidly. I reversed along the crown of the road for some distance until I thought I was back at where she had been standing then I pulled the wheel down so the car came in near the kerb. Just at that, I was conscious of a jarring bump.'

Dowdall raised his hand to signal he needed him to slow down so he could note his exact words at this critical juncture. 'I've got you pulling into the kerb then being "conscious of a jarring bump". Is that correct?'

'Yes. And the exhaust made a different sound. I wondered what was causing it and got my torch out to check. After I opened the door and was about to put my foot on the ground, I was horrified to see a face looking up at me from under the running board. If I had put my foot down, I would have stood on her hair which looked all matted. I frantically clambered out and knelt down. It was Katie Murphy. Blood was bubbling in her open mouth and I realised she had died when I saw it well up to her lips then recede. I lay down on the road and pulled her shoulders to try to drag her out from under the car, but it was no use. She was held securely and I felt sick with fear so I went round to the other side of the car to get hold of her legs. They were twisted and disjointed. It was just the same. When I pulled at them she didn't budge, and it occurred to me her clothes must have been tangled up in the propeller shaft. I pulled her clothes this way and that but it made no difference. I was in a panic and must have walked around the car a dozen times trying to work out what to do. I shone the torch onto her head and it was obvious she was dead. As the body was quite near the front wheels, I thought the best thing to do was to reverse the car to see if that would dislodge her. I put the car in reverse and backed slowly over the body waiting for the front wheels to rise as they passed over her but after moving a couple of car lengths nothing happened so I got out to have another look but the body was still in the same position. I tried tugging and pulling again but it was hopeless and by that time I was sick with fear, worry and horror. I got into the car again and drove it forward again, a couple of car lengths, but that did not have the desired result either. When I reversed again, the engine started to bark and that was when the silencer came off completely. I was really panicking now and put the car in first gear, revved the engine up and it jumped forward. I did not feel the rear wheels go over the body, but when I got out this time, I discovered that she was lying behind the car on the road. I did not know what to do and was overwhelmed by the catastrophe. I sat there for a while and the only vehicle that passed was a dust cart going the other way which didn't stop. After a while, I tried hard to focus clearly but my mind would not think properly. I have no idea how long I sat there for, but then thought the best thing to do was to leave the scene. When I drove off, the car was making a noise like a machine gun so I pulled in to make a temporary repair then drove to Cumberland Street and tried to straighten myself out. Once I had decided to do that, there was no way back and I had lost all track of time.'

He finished talking and Dowdall eventually stopped writing. They sat in silence for a while until Dowdall again started packing up to leave. Just before he did so, he looked his client straight in the eye before asking him an important direct question.

'What was the nature of your relationship with Katie Murphy?'

Robertson shifted uncomfortably in his seat. 'Friends. Just good friends.'

Dowdall noted the answer without comment. 'I am going to engage counsel to act for you at the forthcoming trial and am hoping that John Cameron, King's Counsel, is available. If he is, I have to tell you now, he is not a man who will tolerate any kind of dissembling behaviour. Do you understand what I mean when I say that?'

Robertson nodded.

'In my view, what had previously gone on between you and the deceased is going to be the most important issue in this case. Are you aware that neither I nor any counsel prepared to take your case on will expect to receive any payment for their services?'

Robertson shook his head and said he didn't know about things like that.

'Alright. The reason I asked you that is to see if you agree that it would be unreasonable of you to expect your legal advisers to act for you if you are not being open and honest with them. That would be unfair and an insult to them.'

Robertson had slumped forward again. He looked up, taking his hands away from his forehead. His face had a defeated, pained look. 'Mr Dowdall, is this conversation confidential? Really and truly confidential?'

'Of course.'

'In that case, Katie Murphy and I were more than good friends if you know what I mean.'

'I do.'

'Will I have to tell my counsel that as well? I was hoping that would not be made public.'

'I can't speak for counsel, but that's very likely something he might think was relevant. I'm sure you can see why.'

Robertson was relieved. Relieved that he had not yet had to reveal his inner conflict with *Ronald* and that he may yet survive this ordeal without ever truly disclosing his secret hidden turmoil.

After Robertson had been taken away by his escort, Dowdall sat for longer than needed in the fetid atmosphere of the cramped little room, digesting what his latest client had just told him. In his mind, he went back to his meeting with the Chief Inspector and what he had to say about him. Here was a man who had gone from one extreme – devout, teetotal, non-smoking and moralistic – to another – stealing, adultery, lies and maybe even murder – and so far, there was no clear explanation. Would there ever be? Was it because one lie leads to another and so on? Perhaps, like power, lies corrupt and absolute lies corrupt absolutely?

For most of the public, justice was a smooth-sided monolithic slab of solid truth with no awkward, jagged edges of innocence. You had to be either *completely* guilty or *completely* innocent. Dowdall considered how different it all was in practice where there were often shades and percentages of guilt. *My client pleads eighty three percent guilty to charge one on the indictment, M'Lud!*

This one stood out from the other cases he'd been involved in. If innocent of anything, it had to have been in segments of the minor charges – not stealing the Austin from where it had been taken from and not breaking into the garage to steal logbooks –rather than the murder charge which was either an arrogant, premeditated homicide or a devastating, careless mishap.

Dowdall went to the car park to sit in the car and add his footnote thoughts to the hastily scribbled precognition.

On this account, the client is not guilty of murder, having no mens rea, no intention to kill. Whether a jury is going to believe it is another matter. He claims to have met the deceased by chance, so in this case, 'going to see a blonde' was actually true, and on the very night he had decided to rid himself of the stolen car. It's also unfortunate that she threatened to tell everyone about him. Not heard the word 'sherrick' for a while, but it's not too difficult to see a motive for murder emerging from the known facts, not that the client would seem to accept that. Possibly blackmail? Why not call for help rather than drive over the body again, and how could he be so sure she was already dead when he did that? The client seemed anxious to tell me she was already dead when he stepped out of the car after the 'jarring bump'.

Back in his single cell, Robertson too contemplated his situation. Not as a murderer accused facing state execution but as one of the Elect, looking forward to the next world.

I really can't tell Dowdall or anyone else what's been going on. Nobody would believe it for a start and even if they pretended to, it would make no difference. The only way I can get through this tribulation is to tell them what they imagine fits their facts and if that works, fine. If it doesn't, I'm completely in the hands of The Lord, not that any of them, Dowdall or that King's Counsel he seems so excited about getting, would know anything about His fundamental truth. Yes, Dowdall wants me to tell the truth! Does he mean the truth about this case or the truth that he and his Kings Counsel can search and hunt for as much as they like? The real truth, His Truth, is the only one that matters is that all of this doesn't mean anything in the eyes of my Saviour. It's as meaningless as a life lived in the Gorbals. Only Us Few can clearly see everything from above and the Lord knows I can only go along with their false reality for so long.

He began reciting the words of the 118th psalm: 'The Lord is my strength and song and is become my salvation. The voice of rejoicing and salvation is in the tabernacle of the righteous. The right hand of the Lord is exalted. The right hand of the Lord doeth valiantly. I shall not die but live and declare the works of the Lord. The Lord hath chastened me sore but he hath not given me over unto death. Open to me the gates of righteousness, I will go into them and I will praise the Lord. This gate of the Lord into which the righteous shall enter. I will praise thee, for thou hath heard me and art become my salvation. The stone which the builders refused is become the headstone of the corner. This is the Lord's doing. It is marvellous in our eyes.'

Chapter 17

When travelling by rail from Glasgow Queen Street to Edinburgh, the trick was to find a carriage at the rear to avoid the smoky discharge from the train at the front which sometimes smelled like rotten eggs.

Dowdall's secretary, Evelyn, had phoned the day before to speak to one of the clerks at the Faculty of Advocates. She requested the services of John Cameron, King's Counsel and Dean of Faculty – should he be available – to lead for the defence in Robertson's trial. It looked likely, hence Dowdall's trip that late autumnal day.

Leaving Waverley Station in Edinburgh, he walked up Advocates' Close to Parliament House and the Royal Mile as he always did, being an opportunity for much needed exercise. He marched briskly up all the stairs to the top, only pausing briefly to take in the stone inscription engraved above a doorway in 1882 which read 'He That Tholes Overcomes'. He recalled once descending those same stairs with the man he was now hoping to instruct in the case of *His Majesty's Advocate v James Ronald Robertson* and they had stopped underneath the same sandstone carving. Having often privately considered its meaning in times of stress, Dowdall suddenly asked him what it conveyed to him. Typical of Cameron, he re-read it then walked on, mulling it over as he descended the multitude of steps, all the time Dowdall expecting an erudite response – probably laced with historical and biblical references. They were at the foot of the stairs, where the close meets Cockburn Street, before Cameron spoke. 'It's an old Scotch proverb that means only fools and weaklings ever give up on something they believe in.'

Dowdall thought it an interesting take on what he had

always seen as a prosaic 'keep trying and never give up until you win', his answer perhaps revealing how Cameron's clinically forensic mind was actually abetted by a quixotic, almost idealistic determination. As young male Camerons were sometimes inclined to say, the surname is an anagram of 'romance', not that Jock Cameron was ever heard to utter it.

Crossing the Royal Mile at St Giles, Dowdall recalled Cameron's response, then thought about his client's explanation for events in Prospecthill Road that early morning in July of that year. Robertson was certainly no weakling, but was he a fool to expect a Glasgow jury to believe it had been a tragic accident?

He crossed over and as he entered Parliament House, an image of a mob, incensed by news of the union with England over two hundred years before, came to him. Once inside, particularly when he descended the stairs, his second familiar vision was of parliamentarians desperately scurrying out of rear doors to escape the mob's wrath.

He made his way to the main hall where the well stacked coal fire glowed hospitably. Pairs of counsel paced up and down the hall confidentially discussing cases under the great trussed roof and intricate stained-glass window in the southern gable. Cameron's clerk awaited Dowdall's arrival and, on seeing him at the hall doorway, bade him a hurried welcome then ushered him to a consultation room downstairs with ancient oak boards that creaked in unison with every step. As Dowdall entered the room, Cameron stood up and proffered his hand which Dowdall shook before sitting down.

Being two ex-navy men, they began by swapping scraps of information about former colleagues who had survived Dunkirk and the Malta run only to die peacefully and undramatically in bed, or about clients who manufactured war service records, desperate to lessen impending custodial sentences. Dowdall passed on the recent tale of a plea gone wrong where an accused was charged in the Stipendiary Magistrates court in Glasgow. In the course of his mitigatory address, his lawyer alluded to his client's wartime service with a tank regiment, piquing the magistrate's interest.

'Find out from your client which armoured regiment he was in before I pass sentence,' he ordered imperiously.

After a brief dock consultation between solicitor and client, the lawyer spoke uneasily, conscious that his plea was veering from mitigation to aggravation. 'Thank you, your honour. I have checked with my client who tells me he was with Army Group Centre in the 2nd Panzer Division when he was captured by British forces in Normandy in 1944.'

Cameron smiled briefly at the tale, which for him was a rare occurrence and was akin to him letting go of the iron grip he had on his emotions.

Small talk over, Cameron confirmed he would make himself available for Robertson's trial which had a likely starting date in early November. He said he also spoken to junior counsel, a young Jewish man, Manny Kissen, who was also prepared to 'clear the decks' of all else to become involved in the case. Dowdall gave Cameron a potted version of the circumstances as he sat back, his eyes occasionally closing in deep concentration, listening intently to what his instructing solicitor had to say. Once Dowdall had finished talking, Cameron remained motionless, evidently deep in thought before reacting.

'From what you say, this Robertson fellow is a bit of an enigma. On the one hand, he's presentable and has a stable background. On the other, he's obviously got an odd, dishonest streak in him which hardly befits a serving police officer and the jury's not going to like that at all. At this juncture, the case must hinge on him being as open and honest as he can be if he has any chance of escaping the rope. You say he has now acknowledged he had had an adulterous relationship with the dead woman. That has to be a step in the right direction. What's the second child called – did you say it's Andrew?'

Cameron continued after Dowdall confirmed the name. 'Sounds to me that baby Andrew is going to be very important in all of this and our client has to be sensible about acknowledging that – along with candidly admitting he's the child's father, otherwise the jury's going to disbelieve all this stuff about it being accidental. We shall need a forensic pathologist and an experienced consulting engineer to give evidence about the likelihood of our client's narrative of events being accurate, and, from our perspective, credible.'

'What sort of person is he? Describe him to me and tell me his good points and his bad points.' Cameron sat back in a well- worn burgundy Chesterfield chair, planted his arms on it at chest height and closed his eyes in rapt concentration as Dowdall spoke again.

'He's a fine big fellow. Tall, handsome and normally well turned out, according to his Chief Inspector at Oxford Street Police Office in the Gorbals. His good points? Well, up until now, he was seen as the embodiment of reliability and honesty, a genuine family man devoted to the welfare of his wife and children.'

Cameron opened his eyes. 'What about his devotion to his religious sect? Do you think that's on the credit or debit side of his character?'

Dowdall was puzzled. 'Would that not normally be on the credit side?'

Cameron considered the point. 'Yes, in my experience it should. However, during the last war, I came to know many good men, some devout believers, some not, and whilst professing a belief in a particular sect, religion or God was often a source of inner strength to them, it made no difference whatsoever when it really mattered. It struck me that atheists habitually demonstrated just as much gumption as their believer colleagues and sometimes seemed even steadier under fire. I know you're a believer. Did you notice any obvious distinctions in your shipmates' conduct, as regards their faith, when it came to times of stress?'

Dowdall considered the matter, all the time wondering where the distinguished Dean of the Faculty of Advocates was heading with this train of thought. 'On a personal level, I certainly gained some comfort in my faith, but I tend to agree that it was generally impossible to distinguish between how believers and non-believers acted when U-boats were active around a convoy. You'll know that yourself, Jock. When the chips are down, we're all in it together.'

'Very true. People are people the world over but as someone once said, when it comes to matters of religion, the real enemy is extremism.'

Dowdall now realised what Cameron was thinking all along. 'You are wondering if our client is in too deep and that has completely clouded his judgement?

'In a word, yes.'

'Surely not!'

Cameron reached into the pocket of his battered and shiny old *westcot* and retrieved a solid gold hunter pocket watch at the end of a rose gold Albert chain. He depressed the watch's top button, springing open the outer plate, then he squinted at the dial. 'Got to go, Doodles, have clients to see. Ones that actually pay my bills!'

'Jock, I'm grateful you and young Mr Kissen are continuing the great tradition of the Bar in ensuring no one faces a serious charge on their own.' It was Cameron's turn to wonder what his instructing solicitor was going to say next. Dowdall continued. 'Your reward will surely follow in the next world ... but only if you have enough faith to believe in it!'

Retracing his steps down Advocates' Close, Dowdall began thinking about Cameron's curious take on religious extremism. Could fanaticism have led to Robertson's disgrace and downfall? Dowdall thought it unlikely, but at that early stage, he wasn't to know what the future would hold. He dismissed the notion then began wondering who he should instruct as defence witnesses and decided to call some colleagues for advice as soon as he got back to the office. Pausing only to acknowledge his favourite sandstone inscription on the way down, he was soon back on a train to Glasgow, travelling second class in a carriage at the rear as always, in order to keep expenses to a minimum.

After all, he was getting paid for none of this work and in addition would also be liable for the fee notes rendered by expert witnesses, should they submit any. In his experience though, they always sought payment, not having the same deep interest in the outcome of the case or the same direct, visceral connection with the man whose life was now in a precarious balance which could tip either way. They were free to focus entirely on running their businesses for profit, unlike him.

Disembarking at Queen Street, Dowdall realised that something from the meeting was bothering him, again considering Cameron's quote about religious extremism as he walked westwards. Was Robertson's judgement skewed because of his religious teachings? Might it at least *partially* explain Robertson's perplexing conduct? By the time he arrived at the door of the office, he had decided that it actually might, in the absence of any logical reasoning for it. And there was definitely *no* logical reasoning for it.

That was probably the closest Laurence Dowdall came to discovering the truth about 138D, Police Constable James Ronald Robertson before the trial began.

Chapter 18

Janice Robertson had always found difficulty in direct communication with her husband. Whilst he had gone through a Congregationalist ceremony in order to marry her, she felt it was one of the last times he took her or her views on anything seriously, their relationship thereafter concentrating on what was good for him rather than for them as a couple. She put it down to the religious beliefs he had been brought up with. Not that he was one of those insistent, demanding husbands who expected her to automatically defer to whatever he decided was right. Unlike some of the other men in his church, he was not one for muscle-flexing just for the sake of it in order to keep a partner vigilant and mindful of God's words and desires, as interpreted by the Brethren at their weekly meetings.

One example was the church's stance on wives not being allowed to wear makeup. Some of the women meekly agreed to follow the directive, some wanted to anyway, some feigned observance – taking secret pleasure in private bouts of cosmetic indulgence – and some simply ignored it. Her husband's relaxed attitude to it all meant she was free to follow her usual practice of the moderate use of lipstick and eye shadow should the occasion require, which was infrequent. And there was guidance on how Brethren wives should dress, one suggestion using the word 'modestly' being deliberately misconstrued by certain allegedly resentful outcasts as 'moderately' with obviously sinful connotations. James had never once made her change her dress or her shoes when attending social occasions at the church or on the rare cases when they went to other members' houses. *Perhaps he simply didn't care how she looked.*

He had never taken alcoholic drink and needed no

motivation in sticking rigidly to that, the mayhem of closing time behaviour on his beat being a frequent and continual reinforcement of a decision made on his behalf when he was growing up. He had been a patient father to his children, often doing their homework with them or reading them biblical stories at bedtime; what he was not good at was the tactile side of things, including with his wife, but then many men were like that, generations of them urged to murder and maim foreign enemies on land and sea on their country's behalf before being propelled back into previously trauma free lives once their usefulness to their King had expired. Soldier fathers beget soldier sons. Comfort is weakness.

Janice's mother had warned her – as mothers tended to do – about men's inexplicable fondness for sex with their wives, some of whom steeled themselves in advance of the deed or fretted themselves into a frenzy when impending nuptials loomed. Janice though developed a calm, practical approach. Sex, as she and her new husband agreed, was for procreation rather than pleasure and was permissible at certain specified times when the wife indicated it might be appropriate. Janice was soon pregnant with their first child, a second following three years later.

During that time, should anyone have even hinted that her husband might begin seeing another woman, let alone having an adulterous affair with someone on his beat, Janice would have been shocked beyond belief.

Or maybe just at first, before the news sank in properly.

Thinking about it now, she had never really known him that well. Like many couples who choose to waste away their lives together in a pointless race to some imaginary finishing line, they had discussed the *realpolitik* of marriage – practical matters such as childcare, bill paying and food provision – but that was it. There was little point in talking about much else. James already knew his fate, his finishing line in the sky already drawn in thick indelible paint. The only issue was whether Janice and the children might be allowed to cross it as well, as members of God's chosen few whenever *their* time came. As a couple they had never discussed *wanting* to stay together. That just wasn't done in a marriage like theirs.

'I know I can trust you,' Janice might have said, then:

'I think I know I can trust you,'

then:

'I've been at the nurse and the itch I told you about turned out to be tiny, dirty insects that crawled about in my hidden hair where only you and I ever go.'

Red faced shame then silence from James. Nothing. No feeble words or lies that kept it all still moving towards the finishing line and being counted in by St Peter, a satisfying tick at the runners' names as he awaits the children to finish their race, then their children, then theirs and so on.

But only if they passed the test.

Then what?

At the beginning of his police career, James had been imbued with upright goodness and honour, a proper Christian evangelist in his smart black uniform – not quite standing at Gorbals Cross preaching God's word, but not far from it, sometimes leaving unsolicited religious tracts in police boxes for baffled colleagues to scrunch up and throw on the wet and muddied floor. *Who the hell leaves these things? Those holy types imagine they know something we don't, they're so superior!*

No, he had become more of a clandestine observer of the sins and behaviour his children must avoid in order to stay apart from all those hopeless souls water-treading in a river of iniquity. Then, one day he got too close and fell in when his Protector was clean out of lifebelts or was changing shifts or was in some ethereal God box making spiritual tea on a divine Primus stove.

Now it had come to this though, Janice dredged her deep, largely unused reservoir of inner strength and instantly knew what she had to do. That James would listen to her was unlikely – he never had before – but she needed to let him know that they *could* get through this ordeal. And she knew how to – instant public forgiveness under oath saving him from the gallows being the first, all important step, with step two being to convince him that a worthwhile life could be waiting for them after the verdict. Both sides of the plan needed to work to save his life, but of the two necessary steps, she knew that the second one was the real problem. The shallow words of forgiveness could be easily uttered to slot into a fleeting judicial contest to fool a jury, whereas no future life together could be lived so obviously tainted in the contagious leprosy of sin.

I suppose he made it clear from the start he never really belonged to me and was only tholing his time here until something better came along in the next life.

Janice knew it was time to be practical. All she had to do was persuade him that he might just be wrong about his prebooked berth in Brethren Valhalla. Granted, it would mean overturning everything he truly believed in – a tough start – then he would have to concede – a tough ending too – that he might be wrong about his belief that the great heathen masses out there would be forever unforgiven for living lives of sinful indulgence.

Now he'd joined them, there was no alternative to both parts of her plan proving successful.

Well, there was.

Death by hanging.

Dowdall of course had been forewarned by Dougall that Janice was becoming increasingly desperate to get her message through to her husband, so he agreed to see her in his office late one night when the daytime staff were long gone and he was on his own. As agreed, she clattered loudly on the polished brass letterbox at exactly eight o'clock. The light from the ornate Bath Street lamp posts silhouetted her outline against the leaded window glass as he made to unlock the door. He had had to think carefully about the propriety of speaking to Janice but had convinced himself that it would be permissible for him to at least hear what she had to say. Anything that could help a client's defence in a capital case was worth trying, even if the client himself was being difficult about his wife's involvement.

After letting her in, he led her silently through the darkened corridor towards the light radiating from his office door before closing it and making the introduction. Her handshake was determinedly firm but decidedly feminine and she even managed an apologetic, sorry-for-being-such-a-nuisance smile which slowly faded.

Dowdall let her settle into the client's chair with her coat still on then followed his usual practice of uncapping his fountain pen and starting to write – ostensibly to record dates, names and the like but more truly designed to allay the other party's unease. She spoke clearly for someone whose partner had publicly shamed her and their children, regardless of whether that disgrace was going to outlive him or not.

'Mr Dowdall, I know James better than anyone else could possibly do. You might think me presently a bit unstable, which I suppose I must be with all this going on and the children missing him so much, but I have mustered all I have left in me to ask you to say one thing to him. I'm sure he's not like any other person you have ever represented before, but …'

Dowdall remained outwardly receptive and managed not to appear to react to her whole-hearted sincerity.

'He'll not bend. Ever. Even if it means he dies …'

Dowdall felt the need in her voice.

'What is it you want me to say to him? You have to realise that James is the client and to a large extent, he decides what is said on his behalf. The system is based on all of us – me, counsel and usually the client, too – all seeking the very best outcome possible.'

She listened patiently, sitting forward in her chair, her hands on her knees and her head angled slightly to one side for maximum reception. 'That's exactly what we all want – the best possible outcome. What I want you to say to him, for all of our sakes is this – it's alright to be like everyone else. God knows, he's already shown that to the whole world. Tell him I'm not bitter and he will be forgiven, no matter what. Please, please make sure he knows that. We can even make a fresh start somewhere else. Promise me you'll tell him that.'

The blend of capable, loving wife and mother on one hand and her impassioned, almost girly charm when pleading for her husband to come to his senses was a potent combination for Dowdall. Locking up the office after she left that night, he thought about what Janice Robertson had said and the way she said it. An old trick, but often an effective one was to call one of the relatives of the accused man as a witness, not to try to persuade the jury the Crown evidence they had listened to was anything but compelling, not even to add something important to the defence case, but simply to say: *Just be practical. Nothing's going to bring the dead woman back and we're not here for revenge. Condemn this man and you'll break his wife's heart forever and permanently damage their innocent children's future. Give this family another chance to live their lives together – maybe in another land, far away from this one. Above all else, you have to give them that chance!*

That's decided then. Speak to Robertson to tell him your views, then, with his connivance, get counsel to call the charming Janice Robertson to explain how she forgives her complex-minded husband. Should that work – which it should, given her natural sincerity – it would help browbeat the jury into a straightforward acquittal or pserhaps a lesser, but still life-preserving, verdict of culpable homicide.

Dowdall reckoned he would plant the seed with Robertson on Monday when he was at Barlinnie, introducing the client to his senior counsel. A jail sentence followed by a lifelong whispering campaign against him and his family was preferable to the alternative of a compulsory early morning appointment with the efficient Mr Pierrepoint.

Surely, even Robertson must see that?

Chapter 19

Katie Murphy had never married. She had been born into a large family in 1910 when Glasgow still claimed to be the Second City of the Empire, after London. In truth, the city's assertion had a very hollow ring to many of its slum-dwelling citizens to whom poverty, and all it brought, came as standard. Coming into the world with nothing really just meant leaving it in the same condition, often at an obscenely early age. Becoming an auntie to many, she was mother to her first child at the advanced age of 34 before becoming pregnant again at the then dangerously irresponsible age of 39. No doubt, the midwife said, she must have thought her fertile days had gone. Family planning in the Gorbals tended to be practiced as much as wintering in Tuscany or dabbling in the stock market.

To begin with, Katie assumed her change of life had arrived and told her sisters and friends as much, including Rena, her neighbour 'across the landing' in Nicholson Street. As women do – irrespective of their poverty or riches, their station in life or their marital status, they become clinically primeval on hearing news like that, discussing topics that mere men would shrink from.

Like Katie, Rena was skilled in the more practical ways of the world she grew up in. Making the fuel in the grate last longer, or a loaf of bread go further, or sensing when a neighbour and friend was expecting again were all dexterous arts honed by necessity and bitter experience.

'What, no monthly periods at all?'

Katie shook her head. 'Nothing. You don't think I could be …?' Her words tailed off, both women assessing the prospect of another innocent life appearing, then becoming tarnished, in the squalor of the Gorbals.

'It's beginning to look like it. I take it police constable Clark Gable might have something to do with this?'

'It can only be him. It's just that it must have happened so quickly.'

Rena tried to understand what her friend meant. 'So quickly? Do you know of some rule I don't?'

Katie suddenly realised how stupid that had sounded. 'I meant so soon after meeting him. Must have been the first time we did it. Or maybe the second. He's a strange one. He calls me Beth or Bath something when he, you know, comes. At first I thought that was his wife's name but I know now she's called Janice.'

Rena had seen this before in her friend and neighbour, falling headfirst in love with yet another wrong man, then regretting it within weeks, sometimes days.

'Are you sure about carrying on seeing him? He's turned out to be a bit odd. What if you are expecting, do you think he's going to tell everyone the baby is his? It doesn't sound like it if you ask me, so how are you going to manage? The welfare are not going to mess about. You'll get nothing from them unless you tell them he's the father and he agrees he is.'

'I'll let *him* worry about that. He'll have to give me something or I'll make damned sure everyone will know what he's done. Word will soon get back to Oxford Street and his wife and then he'll be in trouble alright.'

Initially reluctant to yield to Katie's indelicate and functional attitude to sex, Robertson quickly succumbed to regular, tawdry couplings with her when her first born was sleeping or pressganged into visiting Rena. His dismissive behaviour afterwards often left Katie to wonder what made him become involved with her in the first place; of course, she had little insight into – and would have had less understanding of – his mission of experimental self-sacrifice he almost convinced himself he was undergoing during their many short-lived trysts. With the new baby at her home an obvious distraction, Robertson's acquisition of the Austin allowed their perfunctory sex life to continue, the pair sinking more deeply into a mire of clandestine desperation they had never really emerged from since that first, painful encounter on the floorboards. Like two teenagers exploring each other for the first time, he would drive to quiet spots in deserted back streets; unlike eager youngsters, they then had emotionless, back seat intercourse, regardless of her protestations of lack of time and internal pain.

Exactly in line with Rena's prediction, Katie had done it again and become involved with another poor choice of secret partner, but, unlike all the others, this one had started off so promisingly, her own attractive younger policeman at her beck and call. Some of the previous men in Katie's life had been easy spots as selfish troublemakers, interested in drink, money and sex, usually in that order. But she had often gone against friendly advice, always believing she could see out any trouble and eventually 'change him for the better.' Of course, her naïve strategy had never actually worked in practice but the same friends marvelled at her optimism and initial excitement when a likely partner came on the scene for the first time. She had never met anyone like Robertson before, had no idea what drove him – which in itself was probably a blessing – and was clueless as to how to control him in any way. That was until her second son was born which gave her her first bargaining chip. Yet it had never occurred to either Katie or Rena that this handsome, well-mannered young policeman would eventually prove to be her ruin when she finally got round to holding him to account.

As the first place to draw breath in this world, the name 'Rottenrow' lacks a certain refinement, but as the main maternity hospital for swathes of central Glasgow, it was safer for generations coming into the world to make their first appearance there rather than in the insanitary conditions of home births in the area. Unlike when she herself was born, when Katie went into labour with her second son she had arranged for the child to make his arrival in the hospital. He was on time and an early riser, making his debut in an uncertain and austere world just after six in the morning. With no suggestions coming from the mother and no man on the scene claiming traditional naming rights, the nurses themselves named him 'Andrew', which eventually stuck. Katie herself registered the birth a fortnight later, section four of the registration document requiring the 'name, surname and rank or profession of father, name and maiden surname of mother and date and place of marriage' – tactfully completed by a sympathetic registrar by the addition of the words 'Katie Murphy, Domestic Servant, Usual residence: 139 Nicholson Street, Glasgow.' At first glance it might even have looked as if the missing father's details had actually been added and all was respectably normal when, in truth, he was asleep in bed with his lawful wife when his third child cried out for life that morning.

The Lord, though, must have been in a mischievous, vindictive humour though when baby Andrew made his appearance. Not content with wrapping the navel cord around his neck – in a grim parody of what might come – the Almighty seems to have toyed with taking Katie's life as well but decided to spare her instead, for a few months anyway.

Chapter 20

The well-dressed man self-consciously approached the reception desk and waited in the queue as advised. The trilby hat, gaberdine coat and silk paisley scarf made him stand out from the other visitors even before his fidgety manner and sideways glances made it clear he did not belong there. Ahead of him were mostly old women and girls with babies and toddlers, the occasional teddy boy nearer the front, one of whom was defiantly smoking what smelled like a Capstan full-strength directly underneath a large 'No Smoking' sign. Depending on how long it took for the queue to go down, the well-dressed man decided he had done his duty if he endured standing in line for another ten minutes then left. He would be able to go back to the Hall and say he had tried but failed to see Brother James because there were too many visitors that day in Barlinnie.

With mixed feelings, he edged closer to the front of the queue. A morose prison officer was unhurriedly inspecting slips of paper that some of the girls produced from handbags, which were then searched by a second officer who had two steel tail combs in a plastic tray beside him with a sign sellotaped on it saying 'to be picked up on departure'.

As Brother Ernest waited his turn, he became aware of a small child behind him tugging at his coat and he turned to confront the gum chewing mother about her child's behaviour.

'Could you ask your child to refrain from pulling my coat?' He stepped to one side as he spoke to avoid further contact with the boy's grubby hands. The mother stopped chewing and stared at him before answering. A gaggle of women behind her stopped chattering to eavesdrop on what might be a promising argument brewing. The mother too seemed keen to raise the stakes rather than back down. 'Who do you think you are mister? The Duke of Argyll?' An encouraging howl of laughter arose from the women behind and Brother Ernest turned back to face the front of the queue, hoping someone in authority might recognise his plight and pluck him from this line of vulgar people. One of the officers looked in his direction but then went back to guarding the steel combs and disregarding the commotion; he seemed used to a steady clamour of raucous, high-pitched voices at visiting times and was skilled in ignoring these people, the undeserving families of locked up criminals. At last, Brother Ernest reached the front of the queue where the first officer eyed him suspiciously.

'Tried or untried?' he muttered robotically, causing Brother Ernest to panic.

'I'm sorry, I don't know what you mean,' he answered in a soft voice.

'Tried or untried?' the man repeated with increased urgency and volume, without looking up.

Brother Ernest raised his voice, hoping natural forcefulness might cut through the red tape. 'I'm here to see Broth – I mean, a James Ronald Robertson.'

The chattering from the line lessened as the rest of the queue listened in, this time at the mention of the remanded policeman's name. The prison officer feigned ignorance and repeated his question, raising his voice a further notch in the process. *'Tried or untried?'*

'Untried,' Brother Ernest stuttered, having finally understood the point of the original question.

'Right, go through the door in the middle and wait in that queue there,' he announced loudly, briefly gesturing in the direction of doors bearing bald patches of dark wood where the ubiquitous drab grey paint had worn away through years of overuse by impatient, resentful visitors.

As he made for the door, he could hear the others still

waiting in line talking about him and the words 'murderer', 'Gorbals' and 'polisman' being loudly voiced.

By the time he finally met Robertson, Brother Ernest was tormented but still able to fulfil his task of passing on the message from the Hall.

Robertson smiled genuinely as he set eyes on him.

'Thank you, Brother, for thinking of me.'

Brother Ernest nodded graciously. 'Let us pray.' As they sat on either side of a crude metal grill, both clasped their hands together and closed their eyes as Brother Ernest began to intone.

'Almighty God who knoweth all things, we ask you to come to our Brother's side at this difficult time and to provide succour to him in his time of need. Grant him the strength to overcome this earthly challenge and restore him to the path of righteousness. Amen.'

Preliminaries over, as Brother Ernest began to speak, Robertson quickly realised that this was no unplanned mission of mercy, no thoughtful gesture of support.

Ernest's voice was strained and hurried. He sounded anxious to say his piece then get out as quickly as possible.

'The Brethren wish you to know they are all deeply conscious of your plight and want you to know they offer up daily prayers on your behalf. Have faith He will come to your side and will guide those charged with deciding your fate to arrive at the correct decision. Remember, His will shall prevail! Are you bearing up, Brother?'

Robertson began to understand. He should have from the start. As ever, the Brethren were unconcerned with secular matters such as one of their flock facing execution. He managed an unconvincing 'yes' but anticipated what was coming next.

His voice quavering slightly, Brother Ernest spoke again, posing the next question – the real reason for his visit.

'The Brethren were wondering if you are going to speak

in your own defence at your trial. What can I report to them at the breaking of the bread next Sabbath?' The words even sounded rehearsed.

It was disappointing. Some compassion would have been appreciated. Yet Robertson had to put the Brethren ahead of all other matters. 'That has still to be decided. My lawyer, Mr Dowdall, will advise me on that, but I think I will have to give evidence so I can properly explain what happened.'

Brother Ernest considered Robertson's words.

'You'll understand we are concerned about what will be said about us, should you happen to say something amiss, let's say, about your mission amongst those living in a state of reprobation.'

It had been said. It was now out in the open. *Do not bring the Brethren into your mortal struggle. Outcasts and the ignorant masses do not understand the ways of the Lord.*

He persisted, his task almost complete.

'You must pray continually and trust that the Lord will hear you. Remember, you must turn away from your sins because the Kingdom of Heaven is near and if you confess your sins, He will show you mercy.'

Once back in solitary confinement, Robertson had to think hard about his predicament. What good would come from him confessing his sins in private prayer if he was to go on to deny them in court?

What mattered more – telling public lies for selfish, earthly reasons or confidential confession to the omniscient Being? Three score and ten on a mortal platform or eternal salvation? There could be no doubt what the right thing to do now was.

Truth or lies, death was no real punishment.

Brother Ernest had made that clear.

Chapter 21

Dowdall walked up to the station from his office in Bath Street to meet the Dean of Faculty, John Cameron, coming off the 11 o'clock train from Edinburgh. Like Dowdall, Cameron travelled second class when his services for clients were *gratis*. As he walked determinedly towards the ticket collector, Cameron stood out from the crowd. Dowdall caught glimpses of his bowler hat, court blacks and swinging gold Albert watch chain through the swirling grey and white smoke that had accumulated under the glass panelled roof from constantly moving trains.

The two men shook hands and exchanged the usual pleasantries about wives, families, and work, before Dowdall guided him towards the row of motley black taxis sitting just outside the station. Some of the more modern cabs had their orange-coloured begging lights aglow whilst some spewed exhaust fumes as waiting drivers operated feeble fan heaters to try to keep warm. As there were more cabs than customers, the queue dwindled rapidly and the pair boarded an old Austin which had an erect 'For Hire' sign just outside the drive's nearside window, which he reached through to invert into the downwards 'Hired' position.

'Cold day, gentlemen, it's a crazy old world. Where to?' The driver was clearly one of those talkative types who inflicted one -sided discussion on his fares solely to allow him to express his views on football, beatniks, razor gangs or any current topic he felt strongly about.

Reluctantly, Dowdall was forced to disclose their destination as His Majesty's Prison, Barlinnie. No doubt their flat-capped chauffeur would offer his views on the merits and demerits of the justice system.

'Barlinnie, eh? I take it you gents are not visiting a

relative then?' He laughed at his own, droll observation.

'No, not a relative, a client.'

'A client, eh? I knew as soon as I saw you, you two were lawyers. Us cab drivers can tell, you know. All those years of picking people up give us a sixth sense about the fares we get. I sometimes think I'm like Sherlock Holmes, guessing what sort of people I'm picking up. I'm rarely wrong, you know! So, what's your client in for? Something pretty bad, I'd think, what with *two* of you going to see him.' He squinted at Cameron in his rear-view mirror, then continued. 'Now, looking at you, sir, I assume you are the one who is going to do all the talking in court, so you must be a barrister. Am I right or wrong? I'm usually right, you know!'

Cameron glared into the mirror so that the garrulous driver might take an obvious hint.

'No, that's not what counsel are known as in this country,' he growled. Out of well-developed cussedness, he stopped short of informing him that the correct term was 'advocate'.

Just as the driver was no doubt about to explore the history of the different terminologies north and south of the border, Dowdall quickly butted in with an alternative, rabbit-chasing observation that might have the benefit of leading to a more practical discussion. It would also fill in the time until they arrived at the prison gates.

'Now, this is an Austin 16 we're in if I'm not mistaken?'

The driver sounded thrilled that one of his passengers had hit upon something which allowed him to flaunt his knowledge of the technical side of his chosen vehicle.

'Why, yes sir, it is. She's a reliable old workhorse, you know. Bought her from the wife's uncle two years ago. She's a 1946 model and had a measly six thousand on the clock when I got her, but she's fair put the miles on. Now … let me see'. He hunched down and studied the milometer longer than was safe as he drove through crowded city streets. 'Yes, there it is. 83 and a half now. She's been a taxi since I got her. Only ever had to change the tyres and empty the sump a couple of times the whole time I've had her, you know.'

'And is true that she has 16 horsepower, hence an Austin 16?' Dowdall was working well.

'Yes, sir. Did you know these solid old cars were styled on the pre-war Buick and that the man who founded that company came from Arbroath? Not many people know that, you know.'

The driver paused for breath and, realising where they were, Dowdall chanced one more enquiry which should safely get them to the journey's end.

'So, is she heavy? What sort of weight is she? What do you call it, the kerb weight, I mean?'

The driver perceptibly slowed the Austin as they travelled up the prison driveway so he could comfortably complete his answer.

'As I was saying, she's a solid old lady with a fair grip on the planet. Without passengers and luggage on board, she's well over a ton, nearer a ton and a half. She's about 27 hundredweight if I'm not mistaken.'

The cab pulled up at the formidable prison gates and Cameron quickly disembarked to escape the driver's unremitting babble as Dowdall paid the fare.

'Now, sir, that will be three shillings please. If it was up to me it would be nowhere near that, but I don't set the fares, the Corporation does.'

Once inside, Cameron acknowledged his shortcomings in dealing with talkative Glaswegian cab drivers.

'One of the many differences between this city and my own is the inherent impertinence of the inhabitants. In Edinburgh, a taxi driver would assess the situation respectfully and take account of a passenger's wishes. Should he make it clear he had no desire to engage in pointless conversation, the driver would recognise the signs and get on with what he was paid to do, namely drive to the desired destination for payment –

in courteous silence.'

Dowdall concurred and cited further examples of intercity diversity.

'I cannot disagree. The inhabitants of the capital city are far more standoffish. Ask anyone for directions in Princes Street, they will be helpful but curt. Do the same in Sauchiehall Street and there's a danger they will literally go out their way and personally accompany you to your destination regardless of the inconvenience to themselves. On a more professional note, I should point out our client is not typical of his geographical origins. He is chalk to our cab driver's cheese and would be most unlikely to help you, except when on duty.'

When Robertson finally arrived in the cramped consultation booth, he appeared subdued. The brief meeting with Brother Ernest some days before had caused him inner turmoil which had yet to resolve itself.

Dowdall introduced senior counsel and as the pair shook hands, he sensed the client's predicament, something about him having changed. Following his well-tried routine, Dowdall carried on and outlined the evidence and the client's position so that both of the others knew exactly where they stood. Summary complete, counsel was now free to direct strategy as he saw fit. As Cameron started to speak, Dowdall noticed that Robertson seemed preoccupied, and, with apologies to counsel, he butted in.

'Is something bothering you, Mr Robertson? It's very important you listen to what Mr Cameron has to say.'

Robertson was surprised at his solicitor's uncharacteristic directness and he responded with natural politeness.

'No, nothing's bothering me, apart from the obvious. I'm sorry, Mr Cameron, I'll try to be more attentive.'

Cameron continued, probing Robertson's brief responses to the usual recognisable pre-trial complications.

'If this was simply a tragic accident, why did you not

seek the assistance of ambulance personnel rather than drive the car over the body?' Cameron was being direct with the client; no point in being anything else when he was going to face answering uncomfortable questions from across the table.

'I know now what I should have done, but all I can say is that I panicked. Here I was in a car I should not have been in and in a place I shouldn't have been in either and it all became too much for me.'

Anticipating what any prosecutor worth his salt would ask after a statement like that, Cameron got directly to the point. 'And with a woman you shouldn't have been with?'

Robertson blanched. 'And with a woman I shouldn't have been with,' he repeated dolefully. As far as his legal advisers were concerned, it was clear there would be no alternative to meeting what would be the main issue at the forthcoming trial head on.

Cameron's bluntness continued. 'So far, your position has been that you happened to meet the deceased by chance and were simply doing her a favour in giving her a lift to another part of the city.' He allowed the remark to hang long enough to make it sound faintly absurd before continuing. 'How much truth is in that?'

Robertson was shaken. 'It's all true.' His words sounded empty of reason and lacked jury-convincing gravitas. The client reached down to adjust something beneath table height, a problem with a shoe or simply an excuse for respite, as Cameron's gaze focused on his bowed head, awaiting resumed eye contact. Robertson was patently squirming at having to come up with satisfactory answers to Cameron's frankness. The two lawyers exchanged knowing glances whilst their client's head was bowed. *This is the crux of the matter. This is what the prosecution case is all about.* Cameron's determined look returned to focusing on where the client's eyes should be when he deigned to surface.

113

When he finally sat up again, Robertson's attitude had transformed. There was a more defiant, challenging set about his face, the jawline firmer and the eyes having a resolute, alright-then-let's-stare-each-other-out look about them. Finally, Dowdall thought, we are about to see what this man is all about.

Taking the initiative with John Cameron was at least inadvisable and foolhardy at worst.

'Did you not act for Carrie?' Robertson blurted.

The unexpected reference to Cameron successfully defending the notorious Gorbals tearaway Patrick Carraher on a murder charge in 1938 was a bolt from the blue. Yet, perhaps it shouldn't have been, the client having spent all of his police career in the very same location where Carraher committed his alleged first murder, *alleged* because Cameron's eloquence had ensured a finding of not guilty, the jury returning a verdict of culpable homicide and Carraher receiving a mere three years penal servitude. 'Carrie' had been executed in 1946 following yet another violent attack on a recently demobbed soldier who died after a wood chisel was plunged into his throat. At that time, it had been a case of amply justified hanging long remembered by those who had to deal with scum like him, people like the beat bobbies in Southern Division.

This client though, was unexpectedly playing the *it's because of the likes of you so-and-so was free to kill again* card, beloved of supporters of capital punishment the world over and hardly to be expected from Robertson in his current plight. The stakes had been raised dramatically and Cameron was about it use it to his advantage, as might be expected of someone with his courtcraft.

Momentarily, the normally imperturbable Dean of Faculty appeared taken aback. He recovered quickly and answered the unforeseen accusation in a stern, disapproving voice.

'Yes, I did indeed act for Carraher in 1938. He, like you, was entitled to receive a proper defence. Let me say this though; Carraher was as open and direct as he could be – given his penchant for strong drink, which affected his ability to recall many of the details surrounding the incident that led to him being charged with murder. You, on the other hand, should have no such handicap and I am fully expecting you to have a crystal-clear memory of the important issues. And one more thing: as Mr Dowdall and I are undertaking your defence for no remuneration, the very least we should be able to expect from you is honesty. Do I make myself clear?'

Robertson's defiance looked to be short lived. He looked at Dowdall as if seeking his guidance, then, realising there would be no help from that direction, nodded meekly before answering.

'Yes, I understand. It's just that when I joined the police five years ago, there was still much talk about Carraher and how idiotic the system was letting someone like that back out to kill again.'

'I take it you are beginning to see things from a different perspective now?' Cameron's tone had softened.

'I suppose I am.' In his erratic frame of mind, Robertson had reverted to his previous, preoccupied state.

'Very well. Let us get straight to the point. You knew the car had been stolen?'

'Yes.' The answer was given after a gap of several seconds.

'And instead of returning to its rightful owner – who I understand is a solicitor in Lanarkshire – you appropriated it for your own use? Correct?'

'Yes.' Again, the response was slow in coming.

'You went on to affix false registration plates to it?'

'Yes.' The answers were now brief and resigned.

'Tell me this. How did you know that that particular

registration mark would be safe to use? Was there not a danger that someone might spot there were two vehicles bearing the exact same number in the same car park?'

For reasons only known to the accused man, the point interested him and he smiled. 'I checked that beforehand. It belongs to a tractor in Banffshire, so there was no chance it would be driving along Glasgow streets.'

'And did you have the plates made up for you or were you able to do that yourself?'

Again, he seemed keen to talk. 'I made them myself in the lockup I was using in Salisbury Street. It's actually quite easy. You buy the individual numbers and letters and glue them onto old plates from a scrapyard or you prise the old ones off. All the time I was using the car, I was worried that someone might see the shadows of the previous numbers, but nobody did. Not even the CID who got lifts in the car!' He appeared pleased with himself.

The jury were not going to like this man if he came across like that. Cameron persevered, contemptuously dismissing the obvious satisfaction the client had just expressed in duping erstwhile workmates.

'I don't imagine they had reason to suspect they were in a stolen car. Your work colleagues were surely entitled to take your story at face value.'

Robertson did not react.

'Tell me about the logbook. They found several uncompleted ones that had been stolen from a garage which happens to be in the area of your beat.'

'I found them and filled one of them in. Sheer chance which I used to my advantage.'

Cameron stopped talking and put his pen down. Then he slowly brought his eyes up to meet Robertson's, who initially met his gaze, but not for long. Cameron sounded exasperated when he finally spoke.

'This is exactly the sort of thing I was talking about.

Listen, Robertson' – no 'Mr' now, Dowdall noted – 'if the jury don't believe you in more minor matters, they will be unlikely to favour your version of events when it comes to more important aspects of the case. Are you honestly saying to Mr Dowdall and myself that you just happened to find those logbooks? Are you saying that someone went to the trouble of breaking into the local garage, stole them then discarded them when they could have sold them for profit in any of the more disreputable public houses in the area?'

'Yes. That is how I came by them. After I completed one for the Austin, I couldn't really hand the rest in. They are numbered consecutively you know, and anyone looking at the one I filled in would immediately see it came from the same batch.'

Cameron was unconvinced. 'Very well. if that is your position. Now we come to the principal issue in the entire case. How well did you know the deceased woman? Do not rush into this. Take your time. It is imperative you answer honestly.'

For a few seconds, it looked as if Robertson was going to go back on what he had previously said to Dowdall about him and the dead woman being 'more than just good friends.' It would not be an exaggeration to say that a successful defence hinged on Robertson's next answer.

Chapter 22

Eventually Robertson looked up, first at Dowdall, then slowly towards Cameron, who was unflinching in his scrutiny of the client's face. It seemed Robertson was engaging in some internal debate, his lips subconsciously mouthing what sounded like a name, a name that both Dowdall and Cameron later agreed sounded like his own middle name, '*Ronald*'. After a minute or so, he seemed to come out of whatever catatonic state he had been in, his lips stopped moving and his mind appeared to have fully returned to the cramped confines of the little interview room and to whatever reality existed there.

'There's no point in denying it, I knew her, well, more than I should have. I apologise to you Mr Dowdall because what I told you about getting rid of the car that night was only partially true. Whilst I obviously knew I couldn't keep it forever and did consider taking the plates off it and dumping it somewhere far away from my beat, I knew that was going to be impossible after I met Katie Murphy that night. She was getting evicted and I said I would do my best to help her. I wish now I hadn't stopped the car and I wouldn't be sitting here right now.'

Cameron grunted approvingly now some progress was possibly being made. 'Was your meeting by arrangement that night?'

Robertson took a deep breath. 'No. When I said I would help her with the move, I meant help her look for somewhere else, but that was to be over the next few weeks, not that night. She was in a bad mood and after I refused to take her further than Prospecthill Road, she became very difficult, very difficult indeed. That's when she got out the car …'

Dowdall sensed further admonition from Cameron for

two reasons. Firstly, how could he help her look for a new flat if he really was going to rid himself of the Austin that night? Also, Dowdall had specifically told him that Robertson had admitted pushing her from the car.

'Did she get out by herself or did you help her to get out?' Cameron's manner was brusque.

The client had to stop and think – always a bad sign if done in court whilst being cross-examined, as truthful words should have a natural flow to them. Long silent gaps in a witness's testimony make it look and sound like he was cherry picking to come up with something that fitted the bill rather than recounting what had truly happened.

'I helped her. I pushed her slightly because she was getting really annoying and I was anxious to get back to my beat.'

This was not sounding great. He accepted some violence, albeit minimal, towards a woman about to meet an inhumane end.

Dowdall wondered if the other point might have escaped Cameron's precise forensic mind. It hadn't.

Still fixing Robertson in his sights, Cameron edged closer before speaking; no point in going easy on him. The next time he would be asked about this he would be gambling for his life.

'Tell me, Robertson, how you could commit yourself to helping this unfortunate woman look for alternative accommodation over the coming few weeks if your plan was to get rid of the stolen car that night?'

An *ah-you've-got-me* look spread over Robertson's face. As he sat thinking of an answer, Dowdall began feeling sorry for him. If he failed a private grilling from his own counsel, which was mild and restrained by trial standards, how could he ever give evidence when it really mattered? The simple answer was that there was no alternative and he had to take the oath and present his account to the court, warts and all.

He finally stopped thinking and spoke. 'You see, I knew I couldn't keep it and did intend dumping the car that night. Then, I was going to tell her I couldn't help her look for a new house because the car had been stolen.' Realising that sounded ambiguous, he tried to clear it up, only succeeding in making things worse. 'What I mean is the car had been stolen from me.' He paused again and considered what he had said and added 'She never knew it had been stolen in the first place.'

Cameron looked deeply unimpressed. He pressed on.

'Tell me, Robertson, how did the deceased come to have no shoes on when she was found? Do you know?'

Whilst deferring to his senior counsel, Dowdall felt Cameron was now being a bit exacting on the client, who shook his head.

'I'm sorry Mr Cameron, I have no idea. I'm certain she had them on when she left the car. Maybe she took them off when she thought she was going to have to walk back to Nicholson Street. Women sometimes do that when their shoes are hurting.'

Cameron digested the answer in silence and, without sharing his thoughts, moved on to the next question that he had obviously lined up when he had discussed the circumstances with Dowdall.

'And can you tell me what the rubber cosh was for? Was there something wrong with the standard issue baton that did not suit your needs on duty?'

Robertson was quick to answer; from the pressure the Dean of Faculty was beginning to apply, he was learning what it would be like to be cross-examined by an astute advocate depute.

'Most of the men on the beat have what they call a back-up. That one is small enough to fit into a trouser pocket and some of the characters we meet at closing time expect that you will have to reach into your tunic to get it, so you can beat them to the draw if you already have it in your hand.'

Although the answer sounded reasonable enough, Cameron was not letting go.

'The pathologists say that the deceased had an injury to her temple which was caused before she died. Did you inflict that on her in order to make her insensible before running her over?'

The prisoner's denial was instant.

'I certainly did not. As I told Mr Dowdall, I regretted leaving her at the kerbside and reversed back as fast as I could after driving away for about 300 yards. It was only when I felt a bump I realised the car had struck her.'

The client's impertinent mention of the Carraher case having been duly avenged, Cameron sat back as if taking time to consider the state of play, and Dowdall saw an opportunity to broach the delicate matter that had been preying on his mind.

'I have to inform you, Mr Robertson, that your wife came to my office last week with a message she wanted me to pass on to you.'

For a brief second or two, the client looked indignant before regaining his composure. 'She must know my views on her becoming involved in all this. This has nothing to do with her or the children.' The mention of his family caused his eyes to well up with tears which he barely managed to suppress.

Dowdall had expected the reaction he got. 'Don't you at least want to know what she said?'

'I'd rather not.' Now he *was* indignant and was making no effort to hide his annoyance.

'Well I'm bound to let you know she forgives you and she wants to know you are aware of that.' Despite it plainly being in the client's interest that his wife have some input to the forthcoming court case, Dowdall knew he sounded unconvincing. Even so, Robertson's response verged on being irate.

'I'm sorry Mr Dowdall, but none of that is helpful. Since when was it within our mortal gift to grant forgiveness? That is surely something she must know. Should you speak to her again – and I see no reason why you should – tell her I do not seek her pardon but the Lord's for all transgressions I have committed, be they greater or lesser sins in His eyes.'

Brave, strange words, the lawyer thought. However, experience showed that bravado – if it was that which prompted them – often shrank as a trial date approached. 'We should at least consider putting her on the list of defence witnesses.'

Cameron murmured approval but Robertson vigorously shook his head. 'No! I can only go so far with this!'

With senior counsel present, Dowdall thought it best to clear this issue up, to avoid possible future repercussions; after all, although Robertson was unlike any other client he had ever had, he would not be the first to falsely allege shoddy preparation in light of an adverse verdict, although an adverse verdict in this case would certainly narrow the timescale for any complaints.

Cameron rumbled conclusively into action. Speaking directly to Dowdall, he took full advantage of his executive power over the tactical running of the case, speaking in a direct and incontrovertible manner.

'Mr Dowdall, when you come to prepare a list of defence witnesses, include Mrs Janice Robertson.' There. It appeared to have been done and the client had not demurred, or at least had not been given an opportunity to, for the moment.

As it stood, Robertson had now accepted that there *was* a relationship between him and Katie Murphy, something which would go some way towards establishing the client's pre-incident credibility and would potentially allow counsel to go to the jury without completely insulting their collective intelligence. The best way forward was some kind of forensic alliance between the defence team on the one side and the members of the jury on the other, a fictional conspiracy that allowed the client to evade an unforgiving encounter with the hangman's noose: *Ladies and gentlemen, this man acted in the heat of a very emotional situation, his mistress was going to blackmail him and he could see his marriage and his career ending in disgrace. When he drove off at high speed that fateful night, he was not the cool headed, reliable but flawed human being he normally is, but he quickly returned to being that person, and, having regained control of his senses, he calmed down after travelling three hundred yards or so and relented. Yes, he would right several wrongs. Yes, he would admit his shortcomings and would face up to his responsibilities, get rid of the car, which, as you have heard, was his original intention that night, square things with Miss Murphy and come clean with his loving wife who has given evidence in this case, telling you that she has forgiven him. As a result of a split second's misjudgement, all that changed and all those good intentions disappeared and panic, as you might imagine, set in ...*

With the adultery dilemma out in the open, the way would be cleared for the soothing balm of marital forgiveness to be applied to a lifetime's regret. At least it would be a lifetime as in seventy years or so, with luck.

Cameron grunted his throat clear. As he spoke, Dowdall noted the client's title had been restored.

'Mr Robertson, I have never met your wife. I'm informed she is a credit to you, as are your two children –' Robertson began to well up again, 'and I am also told that she understands and pardons your masculine frailty. She alone has the power to provide insight into your marriage and to the sort of person you really are. It would be a very cold-hearted jury that would be able to close their hearts and ears to what in effect would be a plea for her and your children to allow you to remain in their lives, a chastened and wiser husband and father. You must appreciate your solicitor has no option but to add her to the list of defence witnesses he is presently compiling in order to keep that option of a lifeline open.'

Robertson had resorted to his previous habit of wiping tears and mucus on his prison shirt, which glistened and darkened at the base of the right sleeve. He sniffed loudly.

'Alright. Let me think about it.'

'There are rules, you know, and Mr Dowdall has to intimate your list of witnesses to the Procurator Fiscal at Glasgow at least three clear days before the trial diet. Can I say, it is permissible to lodge a list of witnesses then not call all of those on it, so it would make sense to add Mrs Robertson to the list which potentially has two on it so far, Dr Fiddes from Edinburgh University, a lecturer in Forensic Medicine, and Mr Wicks, a consulting engineer. In my opinion, it is imperative that Mrs Janice Robertson be included, at the very least to keep all our options open.'

Apparently worn down, the prisoner nodded his head slightly as he continued to wipe his eyes with dampened cuffs.

Back outside in the relatively fresher atmosphere of the prison driveway, both lawyers were pensive.

'He's a peculiar character. Why the reluctance to involve his wife when she's eager to help?'

Dowdall was at a loss to explain it. 'It can't be because of the truth. As things stand, it looks very much like he deliberately ran Katie Murphy over to stop the truth coming out. His wife can only help.'

Cameron was more relaxed. 'A bit ill-judged, I thought, the reference to Carraher. He revealed himself as another of those dogmatic policemen who hold strong views about things without knowing any of the salient facts. I must admit, I never expected that.'

Dowdall agreed. 'I have no idea why he went down that road. It was almost as if he was trying to resist forming a relationship with you. You soon swept that notion away though. I'd like to think he's going to be a bit more sensible from now on.'

'Yes, it was an attack from an unexpected quarter, particularly as the attacker is himself facing the rope. You know him slightly better than I do, Doodles, what was he trying to say when he had that far-away look in his eyes? It looked like he was sounding out his middle name, "Ronald," if I'm not mistaken.'

'I wondered what he was doing there as well. Whilst I don't think there are grounds for investigating any inability to instruct us properly, he does seem to undergo bouts of detachment. Ah now, this looks like our taxi now. Oh, heavens, it's an Austin 16 and the same talkative cabbie that took us here!'

Cameron grimaced. In his book, this was serious.

'As senior counsel, I hereby affirm my right to complete and total silence and order you to humour the man by answering all inconsequential observations he might come up with. You are on your own!'

The cab driver pulled up with a cheery smile on his face, inverted the 'For Hire' sign then spoke to the two passengers who were taking their seats in the rear of the vehicle. Cameron chose to sit directly behind the driver and pointedly turned his head to the right, staring out the rear passenger window and leaving a direct line of vision between the front offside and rear nearside seat where Dowdall was sitting.

'Well, that's a stroke of luck, gents!' the driver said airily. 'We can carry on with that chat we were having before!'

'Yes,' Dowdall replied indifferently, 'Queen Street station as fast as you can, please! My colleague here needs to catch the next train to Edinburgh.'

With the engine churning noisily and the captive audience

safely on board, the driver ratcheted the handbrake to the on position and half turned in his seat, ready for a lengthy monologue. 'Edinburgh, eh? I must tell you about the last time I was in Edinburgh …'

Chapter 23

The death cell in D Hall was presently unoccupied. Robertson had no idea where it was, and whilst on remand in solitary confinement would often walk by the execution block without realising how unsettlingly near it was. Exercise consisted of a one hour walk every day whilst most of the other prisoners were in their cells, at work or in the dining hall. The prison authorities were always diligent in protecting the condemned occupants of the death cell but less particular in shielding those simply in solitary confinement. When a man was lodged in the condemned cell, the whole of D Hall had to be locked down when he left his cell, the rule being that no one was allowed to see him. Whether that was based on short lived respect for the soon to be departed or to spare him from the cruel jibes of gloating inmates was debatable. When a man was lodged in solitary, though, his daily exercise made him visible to some windows of inmates in other halls and their jeering, booing and whistling coincided with the brief few yards he was visible to each individual wing at the same time each day, as he walked in silence beside a warder.

Cries of 'murdering polis scum' and 'die ya black bastard' resounded around the exercise yard in a brief crescendo, which coincided with Robertson's momentary appearance in the sight of other inmates who had hauled themselves up to the thick glass by holding on to the iron window bars and shouting through the ventilation gaps – 'black bastard' being a general term of abuse based on the colour of police uniforms. Although the prisoner showed no obvious signs of distress at these regular daily insults, news of the catcalling reached the ears of the assistant governor who ordered it to be stamped out, so the inmates of the half a dozen or so cells responsible were vacated and given special tasks during the hour of Robertson's sedate walking workout.

Feeling a certain sympathy for him, some of the warders made small talk with him, with varying success, often finding him distantly inattentive, but for the one or two who persisted, he sometimes engaged in standard 'view from the front line' type banter, the sort heard universally when shifts were changing in police stations across the country. Sweet irony indeed when one day Robertson himself became involved in an exercise hour discussion with a warder whose brother happened to be a beat cop, albeit on a different circuit in Southern division. As general chatter was encouraged, the warder, Cunningham, saw no harm in passing on and endorsing his brother's views on the cavernous ravine between law enforcers and law breakers. He quickly found out, as he had expected, that the prisoner and he were on the same wavelength.

'I mean, what is the point of encouraging these people? Give them state support and they grab it and spend it on drink. My brother told me about one family from Govan that makes tons of money from resetting. As soon as something's stolen, it's straight up to Mrs Logan's door for money. She's even got a ready reckoner all the tea-leafs know about and the rates are good, ten bob for a radio, fifteen shillings to a pound for a decent watch and a up to a fiver for those gold charm bracelets the women go crazy for. It's a well-run business and her two boys take the stuff down south to sell on. The place has been searched countless times yet nothing's ever found. They've either got a safe house somewhere or the stuff's moved on so quickly that it's not in the flat for more than a few minutes. Trouble is, there's not enough cops to keep a proper watch on the place, so they get away with it, meantime my brother's on six quid a week and has three kids to support! It's a scandal, so it is!'

Something jarred with Robertson and he readily agreed. 'Same as the Gorbals. Any money goes on the devil drink.

These types don't deserve to be included in proper society with all the decent people.'

Encouraged, the warder continued. 'Of course, we see them in here all the time. You know, I think locking them up only keeps them going. They don't get proper food on the outside, so we feed them up or send them to borstal so they get fit and can run faster when they get out and break into decent folk's houses. The other thing though, is that they're so thick! There's a boy from Wine Alley that came up to my brother when he was just about to go on shift, coat over his uniform, no hat, big stupid polis boots, and does he not try to sell him a gold Elgin pocket watch for a quid! The idiot was in the cells faster than Stirling Moss and the watch was traced to a break-in in Shawlands the previous day. Some people are just born stupid!'

Momentarily forgetting his predicament, Robertson was almost enjoying the chat. The trite nature of the conversation was comforting in a familiar kind of way, as if he was passing the time with a neighbour on the beat.

Robertson felt encouraged to provide his own story from the front line. 'One of the best ones from the Gorbals was the stuttering hold up robber. He runs into Shaw's general store wearing a Lone Ranger mask but everyone knows it's Gerry Gibson's wee brother Kenny. He's got a knife and a stutter and comes away with "G g g give m m me th th the m m money" and Jimmy Shaw says "How about you just go home, Kenny and put the knife back in the kitchen drawer?" and Kenny gives up! It ended up that he wasn't reported but Sergeant Baxter went round to his house in Surrey Street and booted him in the backside instead.' As he recounted the story, Robertson was smiling for the first time since being remanded.

Cunningham was inspired to carry on the exchange.

'What about that Evans that was hanged this year? So thick, he thought he could get away with telling lies about that part-time policeman, you know, the landlord, Christie I think he was called. The papers said Evans had a mental age of about ten even though he was 25.'

On the verge of contributing, Robertson suddenly stopped short, the smile disappearing from his lips. The warder wondered what the problem was, then his tactlessness dawned on him. It just seemed odd having to be careful when talking to a cop about execution, society's ultimate sanction for the murdering scum that policemen bravely capture and hold to account.

'Sorry,' he said, 'I got a bit carried away there.'

Back in his cell, Robertson got on his knees and prayed as he had done many times before. This time it was different though, his plea tinged with self-pity and new, tormenting doubt. *God, you are My Redeemer and guiding light. Do not desert me, your humble servant, in his time of want. Give me the strength to face and overcome this tribulation which you, Lord, made me embark upon to prove my love for thee. Let me live or die according to your Divine Will but grant me, O Lord, in thy mercy, that I shall enter the Gates of Heaven as one of your chosen few.*

Chapter 24

Cap, noose, pin, push, drop. The professional's mantra. *None of your killing by suffocation in this country, lad. Leave that to the Americans. No plea bargains here. You'll stand with your feet either side of the chalk mark on the trapdoor like all murderers.*

Here's how it goes. The prisoner is led in, along with his spiritual adviser (optional).

The hangman's assistant pinions the prisoner's arms and legs, the arms already done before entry is made to the execution chamber, the legs when he is standing on the drop along with the assistant and a warder. Some prisons have strap handles – like the sort you see on buses and trains, in fact they're modelled on the ones used in execution chambers – for the warders and hangman's assistant to steady themselves whilst standing on the drop. *Can't have the professionals falling through the trapdoor – wouldn't look good and commissions would dry up.*

Cap: Put the white cap on first so that the prisoner can't see what's happening. It also means that those present can't see the agony of the prisoner's facial contortions as he dies.

Noose: Place the three-quarter-inch Italian hemp smoothed with molten gutta-percha around the prisoner's neck and adjust it. Make sure his neck and chin come into contact with the noose's soft white russet hide and not the rope, to ensure a comfortable exit from this imperfect world into the next judgemental one. Once correctly in place the noose should be midway to the left of the jawbone. Important: use the rubber washer to secure it in that position to avoid those nasty, gory head removals that used to happen, the ones that sullied our professional reputation in the past. *Can't have folk saying we're uncivilised in this country!*

Pin: Remove the cotter pin when the prisoner is standing on his own on the drop. This acts as a safety catch, never to be drawn until the right moment.

Push: Push the lever, never pull it. It's like a railway signal's points control. Get it over with as soon as possible. Never waste time by going round to the other side of the lever to pull it. Save time by pushing.

Drop: The pull of the drop causes the noose to gyrate forwards by a quarter circle so that it ends up under the chin, throwing the neck back and breaking the spinal column at or near the third vertebra; practice has shown that adjusting the noose to the right causes the noose to slip to the back of the neck, throwing the head forward and killing the prisoner slowly by suffocation.

A longer death.

A barbaric, *foreigner's* execution.

What about the time the prisoner complained the rope was hurting his neck? Now that's real gallows humour. *Don't worry, son, it soon won't be.*

9 March 1950. Pentonville Prison, London, England. Albert the executioner, a real gentleman of the old school, anxious to do a good, professional job, has done his homework on Timothy John Evans without him knowing he had even been spied upon. Albert noted his height, weight, age and the likely strength of his neck muscles when Evans was out walking with a warder. All very discreet, as if the man had no idea he was being hanged the next day. *Under no circumstances must the condemned man know that someone is noting his personal details to make sure his spinal column fractures at the right spot.* One of the great unspoken deceits, like never telling your children about sex or that Santa Claus was just made up.

It went well on the day and the prisoner was dispatched efficiently and quickly in the name of all who demand justice being seen to be done. After all, the man had killed his baby daughter and if he didn't hang for such a wicked crime, who knows what might happen? It might be licence for baby daughters all over the country to be strangled, stabbed or shot and for hopeless criminal parents to walk free.

Unless they were innocent of murder, like Timothy John Evans. Or James Ronald Robertson?

Robertson's trial was down for the sitting starting in November 1950 in Glasgow High Court, known as the Saltmarket. In previous times, it had been convenient to have the whole judicial process in the same small location so that a captive might be imprisoned, tried and hanged all in the Saltmarket, just across the River Clyde from the Gorbals. Even a set of portable gallows were once kept just around the corner in Clyde Street and were wheeled out when needed to mete out public revenge on thieves and murderers. If the whole idea behind public hangings was to shock the populace into behaving themselves, it was a non-starter as far as Glasgow was concerned and they soon became joyous parties, no excuses needed for merrymaking.

Perhaps it was someone from the Gorbals who bought an old pair of leather boots from a workman in a pub in 1910. Maybe even someone from Nicholson Street. Alright, they were a bit musty and needed cleaning but they were hardly used and well made.

Want to buy a pair of gent's boots, chum?

Nah!

I've got them here, in this bag. Look they're a bit dusty but they'll clean up well. If I took them home and polished them, I'd get half a crown for them, but they're yours for a shilling! I reckon they're about the same size as the ones you've got on. About time you got new ones if you don't mind me saying.

Right. Let me try them on. They stink a bit. I'll give you a tanner for them.

Done!

You certainly have been. They came from a skeleton found in a simple coffin in the basement of the Saltmarket, the body of man hanged for murdering his wife and mother-in-law, his remains escheat by the Crown to deny him a sanctified burial. That he claimed to have been a qualified doctor made it worse –murder being the sort of thing that the footpads and vagabonds who lived in the adjoining slums did to each other. Dr Edward William Pritchard had been a fantasist right up to the end, an anonymous letter sent to the authorities sparking off an enquiry which led to his conviction. An estimated crowd of one hundred thousand watched the event from Glasgow Green and the surrounding houses at eight o' clock in the morning and were treated to the sight of the dying man's final, unshielded agony. He had slept soundly the night before, had dressed and groomed carefully then marched bravely to his fate through a tunnel from the South Prison. He emerged in front of the assembled revellers and strode towards the gallows, it is thought, in time to the 90th psalm or a hymn playing in his head, possibly *Eternal Father, Strong To Save* because of his service as a naval surgeon before his marriage.

The executioner was William Calcraft who had made yet another journey north to oblige the authorities in carrying out a sentence imposed in a Scottish court. The vast crowd howled their disapproval of the prisoner when he appeared on the platform then hissed Calcraft as he covered the doctor's face with the white hood, taking care to tuck his long, well-maintained beard in, lest it cause him momentary discomfort for the few seconds he had left on his feet and long hellish time he'd endure dangling in the air. *Can't have his beard getting caught up in the hood or the noose – that could be painful after he's launched.* Then he shook his hand. *He shook the prisoner's hand!* – before pulling the bolt to finish the job. Once propelled, the body swung round, the head shook, the shoulders shrugged and it took more than ten minutes for the prisoner to stop moving. He was cut down just after quarter to nine that morning and a cast of his head was taken by members of the Phrenological Society before the body was placed in its coffin.

So ended the life of a man who claimed to be a great lover and friend of Garibaldi, delusional to the end but confident his soul had been saved from perdition.

He was hanged yards from the court building and on the same day as Katie Murphy died many years later, 28th July, during the Glasgow Fair holidays.

You *can* murder another soul and save your own. Can't you?

Does no one learn?

Chapter 25

5th November 1950, a cheerless Sabbath day in Barlinnie. A dark rainy night with a strong easterly wind making a low humming, droning sound as it buffeted its way around the prison building, changing tone as it whirled and whirred in recessed corners. After *Lights Out!* only the official warder office lights stayed on, leaving its occupants free to read *Tit-Bits*, *Reveille* and *Health and Efficiency* with regulation issue boots atop cheap and grubby desks.

Out of the light there cometh darkness.

Solitary confinement tells no lies. It wipes your personal slate clean of conceit and untruth. You get to see things as they really are, free of evil influence from the outside. Spending 23 hours each day on your own cleanses the soul and focuses the inner self, more true when light becomes darkness at ten o' clock each night. That's when it really starts, the inner self and what The True Path means.

Saltmarket tomorrow, all eyes on me. I never asked her to, but Janice handed in my better suit and one of my two ties today so that I can dress like a guilty man and sit in the dock, begging for mercy.

As if I was ever going to do that!

A 'Lord' in a courtroom is only a self-assured member of an elite trade union, all preening themselves and serving their time earning fat fees and congratulating each other on how well they are doing keeping the whole earthly charade going; all that has nothing to do with The Lord, to whom we all have to account in the end, even the false Lords who masquerade in ermine-trimmed robes.

Janice, naturally, made one last futile attempt to see me when she handed my clothes in but they didn't have to even ask me what my answer would be, only told me she had been at the front desk again. Neither Barlinnie nor the Saltmarket are proper places for the likes of her. I do love her, well, I think I do. She's been my wife now for eight and a half years. When I was asked how we met – me from Clydebank and her from the Borders – I usually just said our mothers were friends. I've never told any of the others, Morison, the sergeant or anyone else including Mr Dowdall for that matter, that our mothers were sisters. Yet, he seemed to know, no doubt because Janice told him when she went to see him in his office. As I told him after that, true forgiveness is not a gift that's within her earthly power to give and I refuse to have her debase herself in front of the heathens chosen to judge me.

That's right, I used to travel on my old War Department Royal Enfield two stroke 125 all the way from where I lived to where she lived, nearly two hundred miles there and back just to see her, without at first realising we were doing what other people call 'courting.' More like friends when we married and I suppose we still are, none of that getting to know each other during that first, mythical few months of bliss after the door closes and the parents have gone home and you're left to talk about something and neither of you have anything to say beyond what you've already said a hundred times before.

Leviticus. That's where you find what's allowed and what's not under the sheets. We were allowed. Well, no one said we weren't and anyway, it had happened before in the family, and everyone was alright about it. Leviticus and Deuteronomy, that's good enough for me.

If it comes to it, Janice will understand if I die here. What's to prefer, the laws of the Scriptures which are everlasting, or the laws of where you happen to live your life, which are ever changing? As I do, she knows that the road to liberation is to truly understand that all things come from God, thus what judges and lawyers decide is evil is a falsehood based on lack of truth, as surely as darkness is simply a lack of light and nothing more.

Let their trial for justice on this earth begin tomorrow. They think of righteousness yet have no idea what it really means. Good and evil are but different sides of the same coin with two identical scenes, obverse and reverse, both showing Luther drinking with a harlot and taunting Beelzebub who has fled to a darkened corner, confused by the other's courage. James on one side, Ronnie on the other.

They don't know it, but their earthly court of justice is going to be more than just witnesses' words and lawyers' squabbles; it's a heavenly showdown between good and evil, between valour and cowardice, between a jury of fifteen sinners and one Almighty being, *between opposites imprisoned in one mortal body, a titanic struggle that only one of them can win.*

Chapter 26

Monday 6th November 1950. A dank day in Glasgow's Saltmarket with sleety rain and strong winds which whirled litter from Glasgow Green across to the steps of the court building beneath the daunting Doric columns. Court squad police officers with medal ribbons on their tunics cleared up discarded newspapers and empty bottles from the steps the judges would enter by, keeping an eye out for glossy chauffeur-driven limousines. A queue for those wanting to see the trial of the Glasgow policeman had built up overnight despite the wintry conditions, but by the time Lord Keith arrived to preside over the trial it had dispersed, the fortunate few granted admission settling in on the hard, cushionless benches in the relative warmth of the North Court and the disappointed would-be observers wandering off to seek more mundane shelter in cafes, libraries, pubs, or, if all else failed, at home.

The prosecution had a list of 80 witnesses who might be called, depending on the judgement of the Advocate Depute – Harald Leslie, a man from Orkney who spoke in that Lowland, Norse-sounding combination that is peculiar to there.

There were three, possibly four, witnesses for the defence, always assuming Robertson would have to be heard in his own vindication. And maybe Janice too.

After his junior, Kissen, had set out the defence papers on the defence table in court, Cameron made his way the short distance from the Gown Room to the North Court, looking square-jawed, grim and determined as he always did, his court attire adding an extra dimension of gravity to an already stern exterior. Dowdall noticed the cuffs of his senior counsel's morning jacket appeared even more frayed and tattered than the last time they were in a trial together and that the discolouration at the base of his morning coat pen pocket had developed an added black blue sheen. His reputation for not suffering fools either gladly *or* sadly was acknowledged by those who knew him to be tempered by a wholehearted loyalty to an adopted cause; most clients were wary of crossing him once a case was underway, unaware that his allegiance outweighed his disapproval.

Dowdall himself had tried to rationalise his client's contrariness. Here was a man who had allegedly murdered his mistress but who had seemingly gone out of his way to express annoyance at his senior counsel's actions in successfully defending Patrick Carraher some years before; it was as if one part of him still acted and thought like a dutiful member of the police force whilst another, darker side to him was intent on sin and wickedness. That by itself was causing Dowdall to question his ability to see some good in every client – something that he always tried to do. In Robertson's case he could never be sure whether he was listening to the good or the evil version. Now that the trial was starting, it was in Dowdall's nature to assume he would be dealing with the good version from then on. Whatever happened, he was committed to doing his best for him, as he would with every client.

As the eight women and seven men who were chosen to decide the case took their places in the jury box, Dowdall watched their differing reactions as they read the indictment, then focused on the prisoner. That's the bit where their beginner's inexperience first shows itself and they react in a *does he look like the sort of person who could have done this?* kind of way. Robertson sat to attention at all times from the beginning of the trial and during the evidence, like a moustachioed mannequin. Dowdall was interested to note how the gaze of some of the women on the jury seemed to linger. The trouble with fixed notions at the start of a trial is

140

that they can be dashed to pieces on the rocks of the evidence to come. *He looks like a proper gentleman* gains downward momentum and becomes *he might look like one but he's anything but* after one or two cogent pieces of testimony. Only the lawyers sitting around the large circular table beneath the bench know what's to come and for the defence, those first few stages of the procedure have to be suffered in silence, then anything can happen. That presiding judges direct juries not to make their minds up until the very end of a case is often forgotten by nervous jurors at the whirlwind start of criminal trials. With no opening speeches, it's best to get straight into the facts, wherever they might lead.

In any other setting, the two dustmen who had passed the scene of the crime at about 12.30a.m. that muggy morning in July might have been a cleansing department double act. Still unsure of their role and the boundaries of acceptable conduct, jurors tried not to show emotion and certainly not amusement as the pair gave their evidence; a woman had died, and a man's life was in the balance – Mutt and Jeff or Stan and Ollie were unwelcome intruders in this most solemn of cases.

Arthur Ashe was called first. *A dustman called Ashe.* He and his assistant Sammy had been working night shift and were on Prospecthill Road when he noticed a stationary car on the other side of the road. It was dark coloured, was parked near trees and its lights were off. From his position in the passenger seat, Sammy had noticed something on the road behind the car, adding that he could have sworn it was a body. Thinking back, Arthur did see 'something red', but could not say he had seen a body and, as he was the one behind the wheel, he pressed on to the depot to offload their night's work of uplifted rubbish. In certain situations – such as public embarrassment – Glaswegians often go into explanatory mode, sometimes to fellow bus passengers –

Sorry the baby threw up on the seat, he's not been well – and Arthur felt justified in adding his reason for ignoring his co-worker's surprising observation, although not strictly asked by the prosecutor. Hands outstretched, he turned full on to the jury before he spoke.

'You see, Sammy comes away with stuff like that all the time and we all know just to ignore him …'

Before he was able to explain further and launch into his passenger's Hollywood fixation, the prosecutor quickly intervened. 'Thank you Mr Ashe, I have no further questions for you.'

Assuming the jury would already have been made aware of his celluloid-inspired imagination, Sammy too offered sound reasoning to explain why Arthur had managed to drive away from the scene of a possible murder. 'Arthur thinks I'm a bit nuts, you see, so just to keep me happy, he said we could check it was a body on the way back. Turns out this time I was right and by the time we got back, the car was gone but the body was still there, dumped like the rubbish we had in the back of the lorry.'

Had that chapter of evidence been crucial and had the circumstances been different – for example, if it had been disputed that the crime had happened where it had, the defence counsel could have made much of his daydreaming:

So, you say you saw a body on this darkened section of road at around half past midnight from your position in the passenger seat? How sure are you and did your colleague's position in the driver's seat not block your view? How much time did you have to make up your mind it was a body? Perhaps you were not sure of what you saw, otherwise you might have insisted that the driver stopped the lorry? And, of course, finally, *We have heard from one of your colleagues that you are sometimes prone to inventing or imagining things. Is your testimony not yet another example of that?*

As it was though, the dustmen were able to leave court that

day without any of their evidence being seriously challenged and, from then on, Sammy's lively imagination had to be given more credence by fellow workers. Amongst it all, the jury could now understand that a black Austin with its lights switched off had been spotted ten yards *ahead* of the dead woman on the road some time before the next witness drove up to it in his taxi.

He was Mr Kennedy and there was no question of him imagining anything and no doubting his credibility. He had decided to go home after working an afternoon and evening shift and was driving along Prospecthill Road when he saw the body on the road.

'At first, I thought it was a bag of rubbish, but as I got closer, I realised it was a woman. I thought she was drunk and went to toot the horn. The lighting's not great around Hanginshaw and it was only when I got within about twenty yards of her, I saw something glinting in the headlights. When I stopped and got out, I realised it was blood on the road and she had been run over. At first, I left the taxi lights on and the engine running so the battery didn't go flat and so that other traffic would see her. Another car came along on the same side of the road as me and I waved it down and got the driver to go for the police. That left me on my own. I went as close as I could without stepping on anything and saw that some of the tyre marks were bloody, either side of the body. A pair of white shoes were lying yards apart at the side of the road and I thought this must have been a strange sort of hit and run accident. I mean, why would the lassie take her shoes off then go onto the road?'

'M'lud, I object to this line of evidence.' Cameron rose to his feet, his left hand extended towards the witness, palm upwards as if to stem the flow of words.

'As I understand it, the Crown intend calling witnesses who examined the locus who will be able to give the exact location of what the Crown think the salient items are that were discovered there. It would be better left to them in order to avoid a situation where non-expert witnesses indulge in speculation.'

Lord Keith nodded in acknowledgement then turned to his right to assess the attitude of the Advocate Depute. He gracefully conceded the point then continued taking Kennedy's evidence, quickly stopping the witness from speaking if he seemed to be about to stray into conjecture of any kind.

Curious as to why Cameron had intervened, Dowdall waited until the judge decided it was time for 'luncheon' to find out why Cameron had acted so swiftly in quelling the witness's seemingly innocuous train of thought. After a waitress brought their food to a silver service set table, he waited until they had started the soup course before he broached the subject.

'Jock, I was wondering why you were so keen to stop Mr Kennedy the taxi driver from describing the various things found at the scene. Why *were* her shoes lying near the pavement? That's something that has puzzled me from the start.'

Knowing how his brain worked, Dowdall was not surprised that Cameron took as much time as he needed to answer him properly. Unlike others who did not know him as well and who wondered if he had heard the question or not, Dowdall recognised that the apparently slow response to his question was his senior counsel's way of counteracting his own rapidly calculating brain. He *never* said anything that had not been amply considered and fully thought through.

'I was concerned,' he began, reaching for silver sugar tongs, 'that Mr Kennedy might stumble on something that might be contrary to our client's interests.' He paused again, to lift two white lumps from the bowl which were then dropped into dark brown tea, lightened by a tiny splash of milk. 'I do not want the jury to imagine what I suspect might have happened.' He then seemed to concentrate on stirring until the sugar was well and truly dissolved. It was one of the quirks of his character that he drank tea constantly when not in court, even with scotch broth.

'So, enlighten me, John. What do you think might have happened?'

Another long pause as the stirring slowed then stopped and the spoon was placed on the bone china saucer. 'There must be little doubt that a married police officer with two children who has embarked on an extra-marital affair with an older woman who has probably borne his child was in a ghastly position. The three charges must be interlinked so that the stolen car has some bearing on the illicit liaison. Had he not been seeing the deceased I don't think he would ever have purloined the car to his own use. If I am correct, the car was required after she told him his child was definitely on the way, so he could be at her beck and call to ferry her around to keep her happy in the hope of staving off demands for money he could not possibly afford after the child was born.'

'I'm still not seeing the connection with the shoes,' Dowdall said, adding 'with all due respect'. The additional words had become a private joke between them after a particularly fraught case during which the phrase had been uttered sardonically throughout by bickering counsel round the table, implying, of course, the opposite of what it professed to mean.

'Robertson was under extreme pressure – both domestically and at work, and a wife generally knows when her husband has strayed. Perhaps not at first and not every time, but when it's become long term, she has to know, and what would the other woman want above all else? For the errant husband to leave his family and set up home with her. It was her way out of Nicholson Street and a father for her children.'

Dowdall was still sceptical about the theory. 'I'm sure the deceased woman had many good qualities, but I have had the advantage of meeting Mrs Robertson. She is a charming lady and the mother of his children, so am unsure of your logic. Anyone looking at our client's situation would immediately see the way out for him was confession and forgiveness, not murder.'

Cameron almost smiled. 'You, my good friend, are either seeing our client's predicament through the innocent eyes of an outsider or the optimistic prism of his legal adviser. He is trapped, unable to meet the responsibilities of essentially having two families and the demands of two women, one with every right to do so and the other desperate not to lose what little she has of him. That, Doodles, is where the shoes come in!'

'I was beginning to think you had forgotten the point of this discussion,' Dowdall said, knowing how unlikely that would have been.

'By that stage, he would be getting by on empty promises to his mistress and the stolen Austin would also serve as a place where he and she could talk privately rather than him having to visit her in her house and be seen coming and going by all the neighbours. She could also get her neighbour to watch the two boys so she could go out and meet him whenever convenient. Furthermore, it would be a suitable place for them to squabble and – unless my understanding of such matters is flawed – for him to placate her in time-honoured fashion.'

Dowdall looked at the stony, deadpan face opposite. 'Placate her in the time-honoured fashion? I'm afraid you've lost me there. Hang on! You mean they might have had sexual intercourse just before she left the car and she had yet to put her shoes back on? That's what the Detective Inspector thought too!'

'That's one theory that fits the bill that we do not want to go near in this trial for our client's sake. Makes him sound like the cold-hearted assassin he might possibly be!'

'Another thing might be that our client may have had an aversion towards seeing his third child. It represented the embodiment of his folly and would have been a continual, unwelcome reminder of the predicament he was now in, hence his requirement for an alternative meeting place with some albeit limited privacy. We don't want the jury to alight on any suspicion that Robertson might be ill-disposed towards a babe in arms, do we? Speculative evidence from non-professional witnesses can lead to many an erroneous outcome.'

The court Macer appeared at the door of the dining room, spotted the pair and approached their table deferentially. 'Gentlemen,' he announced in muted tones, 'I am about to recall the case.'

Moving his chair back, Dowdall stood up and surveyed his friend's impassive expression.

'You know, John, you really are a master of deception. Anyone looking at you as you spoke there would be astonished at what goes on inside that head of yours. Your reflections on life go far beyond the confines of a tragic forum such as this.'

'You disagree with my theory?' Cameron enquired as he pushed his chair back from the table and extricated his legs from folds of the lilywhite tablecloth.

'No. On the contrary, I find it highly plausible and sincerely hope that the members of the jury have been excluded from coming to the same conclusion by your timely intervention. Not that any of them are likely to have the same thought processes as you obviously have.'

Standing up, removing the linen napkin from his collar and placing it on the table, Dowdall added, 'That is, of course, *with all due respect.*'

Chapter 27

Rena, Katie's one-time friend and neighbour, had had enough. She had smoked all her self-rolled cigarettes and drunk the small amount of cheap vodka that was in the house. How was she going to cope giving evidence tomorrow in a trial about the murder of her friend by her married boyfriend? It felt like the whole world would be watching and listening as she told her story about the night Police Constable *Clark Gable* turned up at Katie's house across the landing and what happened after that. *What happened after that* being the all-important part of the story. Poor Katie. For her it had been no *Gone With the Wind* style romance, instead the usual tale of heartbreak with a uniquely violent ending. And her boys. What was going to happen to them, one asking for his mother and the other too young to remember her? How is the baby going to be when he finds out – which he must in later life – that his married father murdered his mistress mother and left her broken and lifeless remains lying obscenely on a public road for all to see, whilst his only cowardly thought was to get away from her as fast as he could? If Constable Gable somehow doesn't swing for this, I'll wait until the boys are old enough then tell them all the horrible details so that they hunt him down, wherever he might be, and get justice for their poor, trusting mum who only dreamed of living in some never-never land where her boys could get fed and, for once, somebody actually loved her.

Or that somewhere in this cruel and vicious world the child has a half-sister and half-brother. What if they ever met?

Small, skinny teenager in hand-me-downs from his older brother walks up to a well-dressed, well-spoken brother and sister out spending money in town on a busy Saturday afternoon. 'Hello, we've never met before but I know we've got the same evil father ...'

Rena carried a battered old kettle with a blackened, fragile base to the sink and turned the tap on but nothing came out apart from gurgling noises then drips of brown coloured rust. After she reached underneath and clattered the pipe from the street mains with a hammer, the tap grudgingly spat out more corroded liquid which gradually became clearer as water rinsed the sediment from inside. After a minute she removed the kettle's ill-fitting lid by gripping a small protruding pin between thumb and forefinger – the green plastic lid handle long gone – and let the brown tinged water flow into the body of the kettle.

A cup of tea before bed might help her sleep, but probably not.

There was so much to think about, so many memories, bad ones as it turned out, of the many nights when Katie would chap on her door and ask if she'd *keep an eye on* Anthony, her son, born to yet another man who had vanished like the detail of a dream half remembered in the morning. *More like a nightmare though – except you don't forget them.*

Settling into a wobbly bed recess and pulling up the grimy bedclothes over her bed socks and dressing gown, she sipped her tea and wondered what questions she would face the following day in court, should she actually decide to go.

That first night, when Robertson chucked those two chancers out. That must get a mention. Or the almost nightly favours Katie asked her to do when she was seeing him, going next door to shoosh Anthony to sleep when he woke up and cried for her. Or when she wondered if she might be expecting for a second time – that was a real shock! – then went into Rottenrow and came out with that helpless wee bundle that will never know her again. Or after he turned up with the shiny motor with the leathery smelling seats and the squeaky brakes that told you he'd pulled up nearby, Katie coming to the door seconds later then disappearing for most of the night. She'd come in all happy at first, and then … not so happy. Towards the end she was worried about something and sometimes, she was angry. She never said much about it but after the welfare cut her money, she told me she tried to be reasonable with him and he started giving her a couple of bob every so often. It was the least he could do as she never grassed him in to them after he begged her not to. Rather live in poverty than let him down in public, so she would. The ungrateful rat never seems to have realised how loyal she was. I think that's because Katie always thought her luck would change one day, you know, just as he was magicked here that first night, the poor, desperate, big-hearted woman still dreamed of him whisking her off to a better place to live with her and her two boys once he'd left thon wife of his. Fat chance of that! I even told her that, not that it matters now, but the day will come when women like us get our just rewards instead of black eyes and fat lips most weekends.

The time she came back and told me he was married, now there was a night! '*Chuck him and chuck him now!* I told her but she just started bubbling and chain smoking and shaking. '*Katie, you've got to dump him! He'll never leave his wife and kids*' I said. '*They never do! Get out now!*' And what did she do? She just started greeting and shaking again like she had the DTs. I grabbed her shoulders and shouted at her '*Katie, listen to me! He's no good for you! You have to get him out your life now!*' And what does the stupid, starry-eyed woman do?

She stops shaking, wipes her face with the sleeve of her blouse, stubs her fag out, looks me in the eye and says '*Rena, I can't.*'

'*Why not? For Christ's sake Katie you're seven years older than him and he's married!*'

She goes to the lavvy on the stairs in the close and comes back all serious. '*Hear me out, Rena, it's too late for me to end it.'* I think about it and ask what the hell it means and she repeats *'It's too late now ...'* Can anyone that never knew her believe that? After all she's been through, here's a 40-year-old woman from the Gorbals who still thinks there's such a thing as love! Astonishing, so it is!

Mind you, women like Katie are born victims. One man speaking to us in the pub or on the street, *one man!* no matter how old or ugly or toothless or shilpit and Katie was reaching for that stupid plastic cigarette holder she bought in the Barras, imagining it made her look more glamorous, giving it her best lipstick smile, taking slow, deliberate drags from her fag like Dietrich – fooling nobody – and laughing at all his shit jokes just to get where?

Deliberately squashed under a motor?

No, Constable Gable turned out to be worst of Katie's many men friends, worse than Anthony's father – who only beat her up every Friday night – or that Billy character that screwed her for a week before he screwed her for her welfare money then buggered off down south somewhere before Katie's brother was so much as able to swing a bike chain at him.

When she looked in here that last night, it was like she knew something was going to happen. She gave me a cuddle before she went out to meet him and said something she'd never said before, something like *this is the night* or *it's going to happen tonight* like it was decision time for him and her.

Not that I'll be telling that to anybody, especially not those wig-wearers in court. You see, I've got to stick to the rules. People from the Gorbals just don't squeal on anybody, even if they've murdered your brother or your sister or your weak and defenceless next door neighbour friend. It's just not done. It goes against what we stand for here and whilst there will be some who understand if I do speak up, it still won't stop the finger pointing, the public washhouse whispers, the broken windows or the fact that I let the Gorbals down by grassing on somebody, even a shit like him. That time the CID picked me up and made me go to the ID parade where I picked him out, all I can say is that I was still in shock after seeing Katie in the city morgue and got an idea what he'd done to her. I'm not going to pick him out tomorrow though if I decide to go. They can threaten me all they want, I'm just not going to stick to the script they want me to.

I really hope he gets done though – and swings for it, the dirty black bastard.

Chapter 28

Constable Morison crossed the Victoria Bridge from Oxford Street to the Saltmarket a conflicted man, acutely mindful of the trouble that doing his duty was about to bring to a one-time colleague. Answering a High Court citation was, of course, one of a policeman's main duties. Time and again it had been impressed on him and others that giving clear, honest evidence was the pinnacle of an officer's functions; feigned – or genuine – illness right up to terminal cancer would be no excuse for failure to attend a summons of such gravity. It would be an unforgiven, career-damaging dereliction of duty to put personal feelings before giving evidence – even if it meant a friend and beat partner facing execution.

Initial training had hammered the message home.

First there's the crime, detected by colleagues or witnessed personally.

Then there's the statement. Once typed and signed, there was no escape clause and you were stuck with it, which takes you to your evidence.

Should another witness – say an allegedly independent member of the public – undermine your version of events, form and tradition dictated you went down with the ship, right hand firmly pressed against the rim of your cap as the waves lapped up over your neatly pressed, dandruff-free uniform. In the *them versus us* jungle out there, any hint of hesitation, any unintended human foible, would be seen as unpardonable, floodgate-opening weakness by the entire force.

Worse still when it's a policeman's life at stake.

After raising his right hand and repeating the words of the

oath, Morison turned to his right, from facing the bench to looking across at the prosecutor, the Advocate Depute. He was standing at the other side of the courtroom, beside the jury so that they could hear every word that he and the witness said. Morison's first impression of them was not good, some of the men looking like weekend customers at the Oxford Street cells and one or two of the females looking too young, and probably too easily led, to be part of this solemn assembly. The prisoner was just outside his line of vision further to his right, and Morison was dreading the moment when he had to point at him, as was required and as he knew he would have to do.

'And do you see James Ronald Robertson in this court?' The Advocate Depute's minor burr dwelt on and emphasised the first letters of the accused's middle and surname, coming out as *Wrronald* and *Wrrobertson.*

Morison turned slightly to his right and pointed at the man he spent so many hectic nights on the beat with. He needn't have worried about facing him. His former colleague sat stoically staring at the bench straight ahead of him, as if transfixed with the time-darkened, formal lines of the mahogany woodwork behind the clerk; Robertson never looked in the direction of his old work partner whom he must have known could have made things much worse for him, if he was to tell the court everything he knew. A wry smile or a furtive acknowledgement or even a sly glance in Morison's direction might easily have deflected his resolve, but Robertson's apparent detachment increased Morison's once-flagging determination to see this torment through.

'Yes, that's him sitting between the two officers in the dock.'

Hard bit over, with hopefully no future self-recrimination or regret if Big Ronnie goes down on this. Only doing my duty.

He told the court they had been partners on the beat number eight since early 1949 and he had found him to be a hard-working and reliable colleague. He recalled Robertson appearing for work one day in June 1950 driving a black 16-horsepower Austin and he had been given a lift in the car both to and from Oxford Street as had many other officers at the beginning and end of their shifts. He understood the car belonged to Robertson's brother and that he had given him a loan of it; he had never met the brother nor did he know Robertson had any siblings before he mentioned the car.

One night on foot patrol, they had spotted a disused lockup in Salisbury Street, and after local enquiries showed that no one was using it and no one knew who it belonged to, Robertson fitted a lock and hasp to it.

'Did he tell you why he took that step?'

'No, sir. He never said why he wanted it. I assumed it was to do with the car.'

The prosecutor had puzzled over this part of the evidence when he was reading the case papers. The accused had used the stolen car to get to and from work, so why should he want to garage it somewhere when he was out on his beat? Was he trying to hide it? If so, why readily offer lifts to other serving cops, unless it was some kind of double bluff? Or perhaps he was making sure it wasn't stolen in a high crime area like the Gorbals. Should that have happened, the car's real history would surely have emerged.

Cameron, on the other hand, was becoming concerned about where this line of evidence was going, for two entirely different reasons. Firstly, there was no charge libelled for using the lockup without proper authority and, more importantly, who knew what Robertson, the most thrawn and unpredictable of clients, might also have been using it for. Rather than be seen to be constantly objecting, he leaned across to Dowdall and asked him if *he* knew what their client wanted the garage space for. He did. Dowdall said it was so he could work on the car when required; necessarily that would have been during the time he should have been out on the streets of the Gorbals. To be safe, Cameron then rose to his feet and objected.

The prosecutor stood where he was, beside the jury box, pondering whether it was worth debating the point then quickly decided not to take it further. Charges of theft, housebreaking and murder would suffice without adding a complicated debate about *furtum usus* of a static, abandoned lock-up to the court agenda for no great reason or gain.

Morison was relieved. Now he would not have to reveal that his neighbour, 138D, had installed a sliding bolt and hasp on the *inside* of the doors and sometimes took the deceased woman to the lock-up at night after he had parked the car in there.

It was a small victory though. He still had to tell all about the night of the 27th into the day of the 28th of July 1950.

They had started their shift at 11p.m. and his colleague had immediately absented himself, saying he was 'going to see a blonde'. Morison explained the term was a well-used saying meaning going off duty for personal reasons for a short period of time. His obvious keenness to offer his interpretation of the phrase did not appear to go down well with the jury. It sounded like a cover up, invented to gloss over the events of that night.

The Advocate Depute thought the point worth labouring.

'Robertson said he was "going to see a blonde" and you say that the phrase is commonly used by officers who are absenting themselves for whatever reason for a short period of time. It does not necessarily imply he was actually going to see a blonde? By that, I mean a woman, of course.'

'No, sir.'

'Were you aware of your colleague actually knowing any blonde women who lived within the area encompassing Southern Division beat number eight?'

Morison was momentarily thrown.

'I really can't speak for him but there are plenty of blonde women who live on our beat.' As soon as it was said, he realised that it didn't even sound convincing, and the judge looked up at him to visually satisfy his suspicion the witness was hedging.

Morison then made it worse. 'But I'm not sure if they are all true blondes!' An inappropriate remark in a murder trial can have the opposite effect to that intended. Dowdall concentrated on appearing to write, hoping the jury might not recognise Morison's discomfort.

The Advocate Depute said nothing at first, allowing the crass remark to hang like a fig leaf covering the truth. He spoke again after a full minute had elapsed, now firing quick questions at the witness so he had less chance to think.

'He had done the same the previous night – the 26th – had he not?'

'He had.'

'And did he say anything about his previous absence when he mentioned he was "going to see a blonde" on the night of the 27th of July?'

'Yes, sir, he told me he wouldn't be as long this time as he was the night before.'

'When did you next see Robertson on the night of the 27th into the 28th of July?

'Sometime after one in the morning of the 28th when the sergeant and I met him in Salisbury Street.'

'Had you explained to the sergeant where Robertson had gone?'

'I told him he had gone to the toilet.'

'You said he had gone to the toilet. That was a lie, wasn't it?'

'Yes, sir, it was a lie.'

'You knew he had been missing since 11 o'clock the previous night.'

'I did.'

'Yet you deliberately misled the sergeant, didn't you?'

'I did.'

'Is it possible you knew exactly what Robertson was doing that night and out of some sort of ill-judged sense of loyalty to him, you were not – and are still not – prepared to tell the whole truth about what you knew he was doing?'

'That's not the case, sir.'

'Describe Robertson's appearance when you met him in Salisbury Street.'

'He looked as if he was sweating heavily, and his hands and uniform were dirty.'

'Did you ask him what he had been doing up until that time?'

'I did, sir. He said that he had been delayed in getting back because the exhaust had fallen off the car when he was driving it in Cumberland Street.'

Leslie effected astonishment. 'He had been driving the Austin when he was meant to be on duty? Did that surprise you?'

'No, sir. He sometimes used the car to go for messages when on duty.'

'Did he say where he was "getting back" from?'

'No, sir.'

'Where was the car parked when you both started your shift at 11 o'clock?'

'I don't know.'

'Was it outside Oxford Street Police Station when he came on duty?'

'I don't know, sir.'

'When did you next see the car?'

Morison's face had gone red with the exertion of answering such a rapid interrogation. 'I didn't. I understand it was found in the lock-up the next day.'

'Were you present in the police box in Cumberland Street

when an entry was purportedly made by constable 138D in the log at 02.10 hours on the morning of 28th July 1950?'

'No, sir.'

'So, if I understand your evidence, Robertson was missing from around 11p.m. on 27th July until after 1a.m. the following morning and then again was without your company an hour later at 2.10a.m.?'

'Correct, sir.'

The Advocate Depute approached the table and placed his papers on it as if about to complete his questions and take his seat again.

Morison was relieved at the prospect. The torment of giving evidence against a fellow beat partner in a capital murder case had wreathed his face and body in damp, cloying sweat, much like his description of Robertson in the early hours of that ominous morning. Having placed the papers on the table, Leslie stepped back again, his head angled downwards and deep in thought. He eventually turned towards the witness. He wasn't finished after all and had simply been making sure that nothing had been missed.

'Am I correct in saying that a directive exists whereby partners on a shift are duty bound to remain in each other's company, where practicable, at all times throughout the duration of the shift?'

Morison sighed. The ordeal still had to play itself out.

'That is correct, sir.'

'Am I also right in saying that Robertson and yourself appear to have paid scant regard to that order, made by your superiors on good practical grounds, namely for corroborative purposes and for your joint safety?'

Morison wanted to explain that some rules worked and some didn't and the men in the front line often used their discretion in applying them, but it all now seemed pointless.

'That is also correct, sir.'

Cameron stood up to cross-examine, asking whether the

'stick together' rule was rigidly observed or not and Morison now had a chance to explain that it wasn't, agreeing with counsel's suggestion that it was one of those instructions that was respected 'more in its breach than its observance' by all of the night shift.

'What was your intention in telling the sergeant your colleague had gone to the toilet? Were you trying to hoodwink him?'

'No, sir. I doubt many people could hoodwink Sergeant Baxter. He knows exactly what's going on at any given time.'

'So, is the phrase "going to the toilet" another of those, like "going to see a blonde" that does not mean what it appears to mean?'

'That is correct, sir.' Morison was beginning to relax a bit.

'And it's not the case that Robertson had informed you of some premeditated plan he had in mind when you both began your shift that night?'

'That is correct, sir. He never confided any plan to me.'

The plan Cameron mentioned was of course the plan to ditch the Austin that night and not any notion of murder. Cameron was setting the scene for Robertson to explain that himself to the jury when he gave evidence on his own behalf.

After being released from his citation, Morison meandered back across the Clyde on Albert Bridge in a daze, loosening his tunic and collar to let the cold winter air meet his overheated body and the clammy fabric of his nylon shirt. The verdict was probably still about a week away, but he tried to make sense of it all, putting his role in context. He reasoned he was only playing a part in an ongoing process that had begun long before he joined Glasgow City Police. What happened to the Murphy woman was nobody's fault; not hers, not Robertson's, not his – but was just part of daily life in the Gorbals.

Just another tragedy.

Who cared? They happened all the time and usually to the defenceless and the blameless, like the bombs on Hiroshima and Nagasaki. We're all part of it. Did Robertson himself not work in the Singer factory at Clydebank? Did the Luftwaffe not destroy it nine years ago and did Robertson not say he had moved on to work at Rolls Royce at Hillington to make Merlin engines for the Avro Lancasters that were used to kill women and children in Dresden, Cologne, Hamburg and Berlin? Should Robertson not be blamed for that too?

What was it that the sergeant used to say? *Don't forget, the country owns you. Do your duty, don't make trouble, then die.*

If that was true, the fault in all this lay with others and not with him for disloyally giving evidence against a neighbour he once shared a beat with.

Chapter 29

Newspaper reports of the trial sold well in the Gorbals, in that a few actual copies were bought over the counter then passed about in tenements and pubs. Bartenders encouraged discussion about the case to sell more ale and kids stopped playing *Sink the Bismark!* in the deeper puddles in back courts, instead running each other over in imaginary cars then carefully reversing over the contorted body of the playmate victim. Beat cops, now adhering strictly to patrols of two, were ambushed with pails of piss more frequently than before and girls playing peever on the pavement feigned terror and ran screaming 'Mammy Daddy, Mammy Daddy!' when they approached.

Most rank-and-file cops assumed their workmate Robertson would walk from the murder charge, but the CID were not so sure, fearing the evidence was too strong. Fingers crossed he would be believed when he gave his evidence about it being a terrible accident following a lovers' tiff.

When the trial resumed, one of the first on the scene, Constable Kevan, told the court of his suspicions after he was able to examine it properly. An almost complete reverse capital 'D' pointing back towards the kerb was made out in bloody tyre marks with the body of the dead woman lying neatly across it, her head just outside the perpendicular and her right leg pointing directly back to the pavement across the curve, her body an arrow about to be fired from a grisly bow etched on the asphalt. It was clear the vehicle had been driven over her then reversed back over the mangled body.

After the necessary preliminaries, the Advocate Depute turned to setting the macabre scene. 'Have before you Crown production 12, a book of photographs of the locus taken in the early hours of 28th July this year.'

The jurors picked up their copies, some leafing through the pages and screwing their faces up at the sights within.

'Turn to photograph six please. Does that show the body of the deceased woman in situ in the westbound lane of Prospecthill Road?'

'It does.'

'And was that the scene that greeted you when you arrived there just before one am?'

'It is.'

'Turn now to photograph seven. That appears to have been taken from a similar angle after the locus had been initially examined. Can you tell the ladies and gentlemen what the chalk marks on the roadway signify?'

Kevan took a deep breath then held the book up in his left hand, pointing away from him, towards the jury box and using his right hand to point to the various markings.

'The first chalk mark shows the positions of a pair of woman's shoes beside the kerb; number two shows a woman's handbag in the foreground nearest the photographer. That was lying in the centre of the westbound carriageway eighteen feet three inches from the body of the deceased which is visible towards the top of the photograph. Number three shows a plastic hairbrush lying on the roadway.'

The prosecutor continued. 'Did that have blonde hairs adhering to it and might it have fitted inside the handbag which you have already mentioned?'

'Yes, sir, there were blonde hairs on it, and it may have originally been inside the handbag.'

'And did you check if it fitted inside the bag?'

'Yes, sir, I checked that it did.'

'Chalk symbols four, five, six and seven show apparent tyre marks on the carriageway. The straighter of them, four to five, run for a total of 28 feet five inches either side of the body whilst the curved marks, six to seven, have a length of 32 feet seven and a half inches.'

'And chalk marks numbers eight to 11. What do they represent?'

The witness moved his right index finger across the page, tracing out the areas either side of the dead woman.

'Eight, nine and ten are what appear to have been fragments of human tissue deposited on the road surface.'

'And number 11?'

'Number 11 is a large piece of the deceased's body tissue which, after it became detached, was found on the road surface some two feet from the body.'

One or two of the jurors went pale but the man in the dock remained impassive, still staring unerringly at the same spot on the bench 30 feet in front of him.

'Thank you, officer. You have told the court what you saw at the locus. Was there something you did *not* see there?'

'That is correct, sir. What I did not see was any debris denoting a possible point of impact, such as broken glass from a vehicle's lights or a deposit of dried mud from under the wheel arches. Such items are frequently found at road traffic incidents having fallen from a vehicle which has been brought to a sudden halt.'

Leslie continued. 'Officer, did you arrive at any conclusion in respect of this particular scene?'

'I did. It looked to me as if the deceased was already in a horizontal position on the carriageway before the vehicle went over her body the first time. I later estimated the speed to have been around 30 miles per hour at that point. On the forward journey, as it were, it passed over her abdomen and legs and when it reversed, it may have gone over parts of her upper chest, head and neck. It may have trapped and torn the large section of tissue from her body at that stage. The vehicle appears to have travelled 38 feet beyond the location of the body before it reversed over it again.'

So much for it being accidental.

This cross examination was going to be tricky; one ill-judged question could easily make matters worse and place the client's feet either side of the hangman's chalked 'T' mark on the drop. Cornered by chalk then finished off by it.

Cameron began by trying to put the evidence in context.

'What you have told the court up until now is, of course, a theory based on your observations at the locus and your 15 years' experience attending road traffic incidents, is it not?'

'That is correct.'

'Might your conclusions be wrong?'

'They might be, depending on some as yet unknown factors.'

'You mentioned the hairbrush at chalk mark three, now in court as label 60. That may indeed have been the deceased's having, as it appears to, blonde hairs on it.'

Having had the hairbrush handed to him, the officer carefully picked it up by the handle between his thumb and forefinger as if it had some hidden ballistic function and might unexpectedly explode or fire off a missile of some kind. He held it away from his body, steadily awaiting a question that might question or destroy his hypothesis.

'Common sense would suggest that item, Crown label number 60, probably belonged in the lady's handbag, would it not?'

'I'd expect so.'

'Did you spend any time trying to work out how it ended up outside of her handbag and on the roadway, with possibly some five feet or so distance between the two?'

'That *was* something I thought about, yes.'

'And did you come to any conclusion as to how it could have left the confines of the lady's handbag and ended up got where it did?'

'Not really. The handbag was unclipped, it could have fallen out of it at any stage after she was on the carriageway.'

'Looking at photograph seven again, the hairbrush and handbag both appear to lie east of the body, nearer the photographer, do they not?'

'They do.'

Time for Cameron to get to the point. 'Might the hairbrush have spilled from the handbag when the deceased woman was struck by the car as it reversed, causing her to fall underneath the wheels and those items to have landed where they did?'

The policeman gave that some thought. 'I don't think so. In my view she was run over as she lay on the roadway.'

'What I have suggested is, however, possible is it not?'

'Possible but very unlikely in my view.'

'You presumably would say your theory fits the facts, but does the location of those items I have mentioned not indicate an alternative possibility, namely the one I proposed just now? In particular, might it not take an eastwards momentum for those items to end up where they did on those specific areas of the road?'

The witness appeared to waver slightly. Might he agree? His answer was brief.

'That is possible, but as I say, unlikely.'

'And might it be possible that the vehicle reversed over the deceased *then* drove forward in a westerly direction?'

Having grudgingly conceded the first point, the witness was forced to agree another possibility, adding a defiant 'but wholly improbable in my view!'

Cameron grunted then strode slowly back to the defence side of the table. That was as good as it was going to get.

Dowdall was unable to stick to his own rule and glanced at the faces of the jury. Some of them looked relieved. *We might not have to send this man to die on the scaffold in Barlinnie after all. Okay, we all know what has been suggested is probably claptrap, the hairbrush and handbag ending up where they did, being too random to mean much in the great scheme of things. But they could serve their purpose and let us have some reason, any reason, to acquit him of murder on the basis of the collision between a living being and heavy moving metal being a ghastly mishap.*

Chapter 30

As each day's evidence finished, Robertson and his dock escort routinely made their way down the stairs to the cramped and dingy cells below whilst his legal team discussed the day's evidence in the Gown Room. Sometimes, Dowdall would go downstairs to speak to the client before he was taken away to Barlinnie and they would find themselves in a tiny ill-lit chamber that was grandly called 'the consultation room'. It had the ubiquitous white tiles, a bare lightbulb hanging from a cobwebbed cord in the ceiling, an aged table which had the names of gangs and gang members from the '20s carved into it and two wobbly chairs. Whilst waiting for clients to be brought from the nearby holding cells, Dowdall often puzzled how each one of the carvings could have been so carefully crafted, some almost works of art in their own right. Surely a knife or sharp pointed instrument – and enough time to expertly whittle a gang cartouche – would have been needed to create them and presumably the accused in the High Court would have no access to the weaponry required? And if the rule is that no accused persons were allowed in this room by themselves, did that mean that the table had been defaced in the presence of some uncaring or maybe intimidated legal advisers? He had become used to musings like these and decided they were due to his brain warming down after the intense concentration of listening to a day's evidence. After he became a criminal lawyer, his wife noticed them happening over dinner and called them his 'brain scribbles'.

After the trial started, Dowdall was concerned that his client was at the point of mentally unravelling. He came across as detached and his answers to points raised in evidence had become short and disinterested, so that there was little difference between the court-in-session Robertson and the downstairs Robertson, both unable to relax. Dowdall regarded it as his duty to persevere though, so each day made the usually pointless journey downstairs to the basement, where in previous times the bodies of those executed outside were laid to rest after the entertainment was over and the crowd had all gone home to ponder their mortal sins. The less involved Robertson became, the more Dowdall was determined to keep him focused. Sometimes clients can't see what's good for them and in a capital murder case, a listless, indifferent client needed special attention.

That day, he heard the jangle of keys and the shuffling plod of the turnkey in chorus with the steady clack of Robertson's boots. The door opened and Robertson automatically made for the creaking chair that groaned when he put his weight on it. He did not look at Dowdall until he sat down then he made momentary eye contact with him before focusing on the wall behind him. The turnkey pointed at his watch, held up his hand with fingers outstretched and mouthed *five minutes, the bus is waiting.*

Underneath the taut exterior, Robertson was the same listless creature as before.

'How are you this evening, and do you have any questions about how today went?'

By 5 o'clock each night Robertson's beard had started to emerge, giving his face a blue-black sheen in the glare of the harsh subterranean light. His eyes were dull, and folds of skin had started to form under them.

'Oh, I don't know.' He was clearly disinterested. 'Mr Cameron is doing his best, but … I don't know …' his voice trailed off.

Dowdall filled in the gap.

'I thought he made a good point with the hairbrush. How it got there is something the jury will have to think about and when you get your opportunity to give your account of what happened, they will have to give that some careful consideration.'

Dowdall waited for a response, but Robertson was not listening. He was sitting opposite him but might as well have been in a different room. His head was down and he was staring mindlessly at the table. Even if just to break up his client's dark preoccupation, Dowdall changed the subject to try to alter the mood.

'You know, every time I come in here, I puzzle over how this table could have gotten into this state.' He pointed at a large, ornate, carving. 'I'm pretty sure the man who carved that name must have been a gang member, you know; one of the Gorbals razor gangs, the sort you had to deal with all the time on your beat. Maybe a woodworker or carpenter before he ended up in here.'

Robertson's head angled upwards slightly, his tired eyes briefly meeting Dowdall's, perhaps to register gratitude that his solicitor was prepared to make small talk in an effort to get through to him.

Dowdall carried on. 'I take it you've heard of the book *No Mean City?* Mostly sensationalist fiction if you ask me, but it served its purpose, drawing attention to a desperate situation, all those men going about slashing each other for reasons everyone's forgotten about.'

Dowdall was aware that his precis of the best seller about the many problems of the Gorbals in the '20s and '30s was shallow to say the least, but it somehow seemed to have made his client more engaged. Robertson straightened his shoulders and sat up in the rickety timber chair which responded with further wooden groans.

'No Mean City? St Paul The Apostle?' he said, showing an unexpected interest in the so far one-sided conversation.

At first, Dowdall struggled to follow the other man's thinking.

'You know, the book. The collaboration between the unemployed chap and the journalist,' he explained.

Suddenly realising what Robertson meant, Dowdall continued.

'Ah, you mean the title? That's right, Tarsus is the original *No Mean City*, but I'm sure no one in Glasgow cares about that now.' At least the client had emerged from his stupefied inertia.

Robertson was transformed.

It was as if Dowdall had accidentally stumbled on something that Robertson urgently needed to discuss and, as he was the only person his client could talk to, he fulfilled a purpose.

Resting his arms on the vandalised table, Robertson's hands opened and closed as he began talking about his faith. He explained that – Dowdall and Cameron's help apart – the secular battle he was presently involved in was mostly subject to direction from another, higher authority. As the turnkey pointedly whistled loudly outside the room, Robertson discoursed on his faith alone seeing him through his current predicament and guiding him in what he had to do. For a sinner like him, his genuine, unshakeable belief in God would ultimately lead to salvation.

Now he had broken his silence, the God-fearing ex-policeman seemed incapable of understanding either his present setting or the time constraints on his meeting. Yes, what his legal team said was important, but it would be an insult to God if He was not granted the casting vote on what needed to be done at a time like this. First ten, then 15, then 25 minutes passed, before the turnkey dispensed with any semblance of unspoken etiquette and burst in the door, handcuffs outstretched and ready for use.

'Sorry fellows, the driver's going nuts out there and I said I would make sure all the prisoners would be out by six. You're the last customer tonight, James, and the court squad need to get home by seven.'

As Dowdall left the building that evening, he marvelled at his client's ironclad loyalty to his faith. That was private and no trouble – except that a nonspiritual, worldly view of the evidence to come was a more urgent concern for his legal advisers.

Chapter 31

Professor John Glaister was a globally renowned expert in the scientific study of crime. The Regius Professor of Forensic Medicine at Glasgow University was a small-framed, meticulous man with receding silver hair, horn-rimmed glasses, and a thin white moustache, his opinion mattering far more than his image. He had given evidence in many courts around the world and his manner was relaxed, thoughtful and measured.

Just the sort of witness you don't need when defending a capital murder charge.

After the Austin had been traced to its hiding place in the Gorbals, Glaister had been called in by the Crown to examine it minutely, spending several days working with the young female police employee playing the part of the deceased, dutifully lying prostrate in various poses so that the professor might decipher the most likely pre-incident scenario. The post-mortem report had disclosed thirty external wounds and many more internal injuries.

Before starting his investigations, he was made aware of Robertson's 'accident' defence to the murder charge, which was taken account of as the car was minutely examined. The accused man's police tunic and his unauthorised cosh were also subjected to the professor's intense scrutiny.

As an expert witness, Glaister had been furnished with every aspect of the Crown case and, in that capacity, the judge had allowed an unopposed Crown motion for him to sit in court and listen to the prosecution evidence as it unfolded. His testimony represented the 'silent' evidence that could be gleaned from the road, the car, the injuries and the uniform, seen only by the expert eye. In his memoirs, he later described his field of study as one that 'intrigues many yet is understood by few' but the task before him that day was to make as many of the 15 members of the jury understand and agree with his conclusions, should they be inclined to do so. If it came to that, a majority of eight would do just as nicely.

The prosecutor began with Robertson's tunic. Had he genuinely struggled to free the dead woman from underneath the car, bloodstaining ought to have been found on the sleeves if not elsewhere.

There was no trace of blood.

The rubber cosh Robertson had in his pocket when he was searched was also examined for the presence of blood, just in case the Crown theory about him stunning her before laying her out and running her over could be made out. It was found to have a small stain on the grip spiral that was presumptively tested using benzidine. It came up positive, meaning it *might* be blood. In other words, at some time since the weapon's creation, someone's blood might very well have been deposited on it *where it was held*; the sort of thing that might be found on a baton used by beat cops in the Gorbals most Saturday nights. That was as far as the professor could go with that and in the hands of skilled counsel, would not bear sufficient scrutiny to support that aspect of the charge. That said, the autopsy report noted a bruise to the dead woman's right temple which had been caused during life, the type likely to be caused by a blow from such a blunt instrument.

Turning to the examination of the Austin, the whole court moved outside to a lane tarpaulined off to the prying eyes of the public. The car had been propped up by sturdy wooden batons on two wheels like a great black helpless beetle, captured and restrained so that its private underbelly could be examined by inquisitive spectators. No words were spoken as the Macer, by prior arrangement, pointed silently to printed numbers from one to 25 propped up on metal bases starting at the front of the vehicle, running along the chassis, and ending at the rear bumper. Once beside the car, jurors were free to break ranks. Some male jurors hunkered down to get a better look at the broken silencer – still held roughly in place by the hastily improvised tangle of rope secured to the rear nearside door handle. Some female jurors recoiled from chalk-circled maroon and brown stains still visible on the driveshaft and the insides of both offside wheels. After all, it was hard not to imagine Katie's terror after seeing a victim's eye view of death by motor car, should the unfortunate woman have been conscious at the time when it happened.

Chalk, rope and blood in a different order.

Once back in the building, the professor's judgement was clear and succinct. 'It appears unlikely that the construction of the vehicle would cause the clothing of the deceased to entangle itself to the extent that she could not be freed by a person of average strength. That might be achieved by grasping her limbs and using the vehicle's running board as leverage.'

One aspect of the autopsy report made it evident she had been lying prone when parts of her body had been flattened.

'Tell me, Professor, why did you come to that conclusion?' Leslie asked.

'That is based principally on two aspects of my investigation into the facts of this case. Firstly, the lack of relative damage to the vehicle itself, and secondly, the injuries sustained by the deceased.'

'And were you able to draw any inferences from these?'

'Yes. I came to the conclusion that the deceased could not have been knocked down by the car whilst she was standing upright on the carriageway.'

'Accordingly, it is your opinion that she was lying horizontally on the road when the vehicle first made contact with her? Is that the case?'

175

'It is.'

'And is it possible to ascertain whether the deceased woman was alive when some of the injuries you refer to were sustained?'

'It is. With regard to the medical reports I have seen and the slides of tissue I examined, it is my view that the deceased woman's heart had ceased functioning when some of them were inflicted. For instance, the injuries to the inner aspects of both knees were clearly post-mortem. Death would have been instantaneous when the weight of the vehicle came to bear on the lower abdomen, crushing the pelvis.'

Cameron lost no time in testing Glaister's evidence. Could it perhaps stretch to include another, unlikely sounding theory?

'Professor, with reference to the damage to the vehicle that the ladies and gentlemen recently inspected, is there not an obvious dent, at marker 25, on the rear bumper?'

'There is.'

'And was that of any significance?'

'I do not think so. It is not the kind of mark that one would expect to find on a motor vehicle which had come into contact with a human body.'

'Surely such marks will depend on variable factors such as the make and robustness of the motor vehicle itself, the speed it was doing at the time of impact and where the point of impact was on the body?'

'It does.'

'In the present case, the amount of flesh torn from the knees makes it difficult if not impossible to say how those injuries came about, does it not?'

Glaister peered at Cameron over the rims of his glasses before answering – not confronting him – but allowing himself thinking time, so that he could be painstakingly precise in his response.

'It is important to remember that the damage to the knees

of the deceased is to the inner aspects and not the frontal areas. The reason that is significant in this case is that it would be very unusual for a woman to stand in such a way to present that part of her anatomy to an oncoming vehicle.'

The court was presented with an unlikely image of Katie standing in the middle of the road with her heels together and her unshod feet turned sideways so that they formed a continuous bare straight line with toes at either end, the inside of her knees bared to the world.

At that stage of the questioning, Robertson's account of events was looking decidedly suspect; time to move on. Having gone into the details of the medical reports, Cameron suddenly returned to what might have caused the dent in the back bumper. Not an unusual tactic. Attrition followed by surprise.

'Going back to marker number 25 from the vehicle, is it your evidence that the depression on the rear bumper the ladies and gentlemen observed earlier today could *not* have been caused by contact with a human body?'

It's all about how you ask the important questions.

Glaister had not said that, but he recognised the ploy, smiling slightly as he responded.

'I said I did not *think* it could have been caused in that fashion,' Glaister answered.

Cameron persisted.

'So, the dent of the bumper could have been caused by coming into contact with a person on the carriageway? For instance, by striking bone?'

'It could have but there would be corresponding bruising on the deceased which would be extensive.'

'So, it could have been caused by striking bone?'

'I cannot eliminate that possibility, but it would not be unreasonable to expect damage to the skin covering whichever section of bone was struck.'

A glimmer of light. Cameron was now looking to trap

and preserve it in the jury's mind for later use.

'Therefore, as far as the motor car is concerned, there *is* evidence on the bumper which is at least consistent with a collision between the rear of the vehicle and a human body?'

It was the usual, expected manoeuvring by defence counsel to present their case as they would wish the jury to see it.

Glaister subdued an urge to shrug his shoulders.

'Of course there is, but it could be consistent with many other things. A vast collection of other possibilities cannot be eliminated here.'

Cameron placed his papers on the table, a sign his examination was drawing to a close.

'I don't know if you can help me with this, but I take it you completely discount the possibility that an accident caused the death here?'

Once again, Glaister took his time to answer such an important issue, the main point of the proceedings.

'Not quite. The main burden of my testimony is that I can account for most of the adminicles of evidence in this case by taking the view that the deceased was run over by the front of the vehicle and went under its wheels on at least one more occasion. If I am correct, the circumstances that led up to that occurring are a matter for the ladies and gentlemen of the jury.'

There was one more point, as ever with tenacious questioners.

'If there is no proof that the deceased was lying insensible on the tarmac in the path of an advancing motor car, can you in any sense eliminate the possibility of an accident?'

'My opinion is that the injuries were sustained by a forward motion of the car travelling at an appreciable speed and that the vehicle went over the body on more than one occasion.'

'Thank you, Professor. You said earlier that it was

unlikely that the deceased's clothing would entangle itself to the underside of the vehicle. Did that observation apply principally to the nature and construction of the vehicle's driveshaft?'

Glaister took time to answer. 'Yes, although consideration was given to the construction of the chassis.'

Cameron paused, not wanting to damage any favourable interpretation that could be gleaned from Glaister's measured words. 'Are the ladies and gentlemen to understand that when you say that the construction of the vehicle would be unlikely to cause the deceased's clothing to become entangled, you are referring to its underside?'

Glaister agreed.

Cameron edged cautiously forward. 'And does that observation relate to the entire undercarriage of the vehicle or mainly to the driveshaft?'

'Mainly to the driveshaft, although there were no obvious features in the undercarriage, as you term it, that appeared capable of snagging the clothing of the deceased so that she might not be dislodged by a person or persons reaching underneath.'

'Are we to understand that strips of fabric matching the clothing of the deceased woman were found clinging to the vehicle's chassis when you examined it?'

'Yes, that is the case.'

Cameron had at least stopped the door slamming shut on an improbable defence which, despite everything, was still open for consideration by the jury. At that stage in the trial, it could have been worse, much worse, but for the efforts of the defence team, the junior keeping careful notes, the senior steadily building a platform for defence evidence to come and Dowdall doing his best to keep a contrary client anchored in reality.

Chapter 32

The court then heard from an official from the National Assistance Board who confirmed that Katie had refused to name the father of her second born child. Years of dealing with claimants reluctant to reveal the whole truth made her as cynical as any world-weary detective from Southern Division, her matter-of-fact court manner telling its own tale.

'Yes, this claim form was completed with information the claimant told the department' she said, sounding bored.

'Is there a reason why claimants themselves do not complete these forms?'

The witness gave the prosecutor an 'are you kidding me?' look. 'Yes, there is. Some of the things they used to say were ridiculous and it was taking up all our time to read through them before pointing out obvious errors, like discrepancies in the number of children they said they had or saying the father had been killed during the war when we had a file for him claiming assistance the day before.'

In a trial like this, once the jurors become settled, any sort of light relief was welcome and the lady from the NAB, with her glasses on a chain round her neck and her artificially posh accent, was playing her part. After her identity had been confirmed, she was anxious that her full title was known to the court, interrupting Leslie when he tried to begin leading evidence of factual matters to make sure the court knew she was not just any old employee but was, in fact, the assistant office manager. She was a small, stout woman wearing a severe brown and cream dogtooth patterned two-piece suit, the lower lapels of the jacket edged in brown velvet adding to her aura of authority whilst accentuating her rotundity. No one – particularly penniless claimants – would choose to cross her and giving evidence in a murder trial brought no obvious signs of nerves. On the contrary, she appeared thoroughly at ease, taking her time with her answers and, whether consciously or not, occasionally frowning at questions obviously beneath her exalted level of competence.

In the course of murder trials, laughs tend to favour the defence, detracting from the solemnity of the proceedings and sometimes lending a reckless devil-may-care, we-seem-to-have-forgotten-why-we're-here edge to the hearing.

The prosecutor had no choice but to call her and was beginning to regret it.

'Is that why you complete the form then get the claimant to read it back before signing it?' he asked.

The witness looked puzzled and scowled at the Advocate Depute. 'Well, I certainly do not complete these forms. Employees at a much lower grade than mine carry out that sort of thing.' She had clearly reacted badly to the prosecutor's unintentional implication that she was far less important than she actually was.

In between questions, the witness removed her dark brown flyaway glasses and rested them on her frilly-bloused bosom, replacing them when directed to a particular section of the form. They were held securely by a thin gold coloured chain which stretched around her neck.

Leslie asked the question again in a different guise.

'Is that why the form is completed *by someone in your department,* then read back to the claimant prior to them signing it?'

On hearing the rephrased question, she put the glasses back on before answering.

'If you turn to the final page, you will see there's a warning about providing false information printed beside where the person signs. Do you want me to read it out?' The glasses came off again.

Dowdall noticed some of the jurors smiling; it was as if

the prosecutor himself was humbly seeking state assistance and the witness was casting a disbelieving eye over his fraudulently completed form. It was much needed recreation in the midst of gore, flesh and tissue on the public highway.

Leslie spoke with an urgency in his tone, anxious to get this chapter of evidence over with. 'No, thank you. Please just confirm the claimant's name, date of birth and address and that she signed it.'

The glasses went back on in an *again?* kind of way before she read the information out.

The jury were sorry when her evidence was completed, the entertainment all too brief, although there had been good reason for leading it. If the mother of the child refused to divulge the name of the father, officials like the last witness were at liberty to reduce the amount of assistance paid – a modern-day penitent's stool with serious consequences for single mothers already living well below the breadline. Added to what the jury already knew – that the father was said to be a married beat cop, that Robertson had been identified as such by a sister of the dead woman – it meant he had to be giving her money from his already insubstantial pay packet. Worse for the defence, it showed her in an understanding, almost loyal, not wanting to drop him in it kind of way and provided a textbook motive for him taking her somewhere quiet, knocking her out then squashing the life out of her under 27 hundredweight of death. Discretion rewarded by brutality.

It wasn't vital to proving the case, but Rena finally answered her witness citation, having failed to appear a couple of days before. 'She's reverting to type, Mr Leslie', the office manager, Mrs Burnett, advised the Advocate Depute. 'These people don't think or act like witnesses from good areas like central Edinburgh or Kelvinside here in Glasgow. It's a matter of honour, you see, and their lives would be made hell if they were seen to be publicly assisting the Crown …'

The Advocate Depute appeared surprised at such troubling news and was about to make a point, but Mrs Burnett held a firm hand up and continued. 'Yes, I know what you're going to say. You're going to tell me that this man murdered her friend and neighbour, so what possible reason can there be for her reluctance to attend?'

Leslie bowed to her knowledge and experience and stopped himself from asking that very question. Instead, he sought her advice on how best to deal with a rare situation like this, not having experienced many reluctant witnesses in his time in Crown Office.

Mrs Burnett brandished an official piece of paper in her hand which she then laid resolutely on his desk. 'This,' she explained, 'is an execution of service proving that she was personally cited, so you're well within your rights to seek a warrant for her apprehension from His Lordship. Might I suggest that Mr Kissen takes it to the Clerk and explains the situation to him to alert the judge about your motion?'

'Yes, that seems in order, Mrs Burnett. Might I enquire how you came to be in possession of the knowledge about these quaint Gorbals' customs?'

Mrs Burnett nodded agreeably, happy to explain and pleased that someone in a more exalted position to hers was deferring to her judgement and wisdom. 'My husband is a former police officer who spent some time in the Southern Division, and until the day he retired he used to say that nothing would surprise him about Gorbalites. They can be brutal towards each other, particularly after the demon drink's been taken, yet the very same people can be fiercely loyal and generous to neighbours in need.'

Leslie saw no reason to doubt her word but wondered if and when the witness would be available, given the stringent rules about a trial being completed *within* 110 days of the accused being committed until liberated in due course of law

– a date now fast approaching.

'Don't worry about that, Mr Leslie, the dayshift will get her tomorrow, probably lying in bed reading a penny novelette or a cowboy magazine. Unwilling witnesses from that part of the world tend not to be next traced to Martinique or New England.'

Mrs Burnett's scornful forecast proved correct, and Rena turned up the following day having been traced to her mother's house in nearby Surrey Street. Defiant to the end, Rena adopted a sullen demeanour and answered questions from both sides of the table in a monosyllabic huff which stopped just short of a judicial warning. Having agreed that she had attended an identification parade where she had identified James Ronald Robertson as Katie's 'boyfriend', she decided that she had reached the limits of her co-operation with the authorities and when asked if she could see that person again in court, she impertinently and deliberately stared at the accused man for several seconds, then, with a slight shake of her head, almost immediately pointed at a scandalised rotund, balding red-haired elderly gentleman of the press. Up until he retired six months later, the affronted journalist would often return to his desk to find messages addressed to 'young Andrew's father'.

That Thursday the judge adjourned early, at quarter to four. The Crown case was complete, and the defence team went downstairs to the consultation room, all three lawyers thinking their own private thoughts on how to save their client's life. Dowdall had not completely given up on calling Janice, even if just to make it difficult for the jury to make her a widow. Either way, it was going to be a gamble. According to the evidence, Robertson had had an affair and then killed his mistress – two wrongs of differing gravity – so would it be right that such a man be rewarded on the basis that his wife should be pitied? If two wrongs can't make a right, three of them might just make it worse.

Counsel saw it from a slightly different angle. Although content with the proposition that the client's life might be saved by emotionally blackmailing the jury, from what the instructing solicitor had said about Janice, Cameron had doubts about the tactic.

The contrast might be too much.

Having a sexual relationship with a desperate, unmarried mother of two living in seedy conditions when he had a wholesome wife and two well brought up children at home might make Robertson appear a predatory hypocrite, prepared to take advantage of a powerless woman then dispose of her when she became inconvenient. Alright, that might not be an accurate summation of how this most unlikely couple got, then stayed, together – if cheap, meaningless encounters on carpet-less floors and in the back seat of a stolen car could be described that way – but there was a real risk that's how the jury might see it. In capital murder trials, the defence can – and some say, *should* – use everything they can to save their client from the noose. How far should Cameron go?

Seeing all three lawyers coming down the stairs, the sergeant in charge of the prisoners quickly arranged for two more of the unsuitably shaky wooden chairs to be moved into the consultation room. For some moments, the lawyers were faced with only two seats and, as one *by rights* had to be given to the client, Dowdall remained standing as did junior counsel. Cameron, on the other hand, sat down without hesitation, moving his seated frame from side to side a few times to check it was up to the job of keeping him in a dignified, upright position. The extra chairs arrived before the client did, allowing all three to each command a small portion of the antiquated, vandalised table. As one of the escorts departed, he leaned forward and tapped Dowdall's sleeve, quietly informing him *there's no rush tonight*. Timetable compassion at last.

185

As more and more time elapsed before Robertson appeared, Dowdall began to suspect another mood swing had taken hold of the client and was concerned how counsel would react. Cameron was not known for his patience with contrary behaviour, even in these extreme circumstances.

Experience, in this line of work, made you slick but insensitive.

He need not have worried. Robertson appeared but was in a low, despondent frame of mind. He sat mechanically on the sole remaining chair without making eye contact with any of the others in the room. Once again, he looked as if he needed a shave, the familiar blue-black shadow appearing around a now untrimmed, unruly moustache. The once-dapper pinstriped suit looked unkempt and creased and his open collar showed a thin line of dirt on the inside, almost greasy in its appearance. His head bowed, he continually wrung his hands together, occasionally cupping his head in them as Cameron spoke in low, deliberate tones.

'Mr Robertson, I'm sure you do not need reminding how important your evidence tomorrow is going to be. You will be required to be in top form, answering all questions in a loud, clear voice. I shall assess the volume of your responses at the beginning of my examination in chief and if you need to speak up, I shall move further towards the back wall at the jury box. That will be your signal to speak more loudly.'

At first, it looked as if the client had not heard his lead counsel's voice. His hand wringing increased in intensity and the detached look in his eyes became one of total isolation. Cameron looked to Dowdall who was about to speak when Robertson coughed, took a deep breath and glanced in Cameron's direction before talking. The thousand-yard stare remained but at least he had lifted his head. Addressing the white tiles behind Cameron's back, Robertson's voice began audibly then decreased in volume as he explained he understood what Cameron had been saying.

Cameron waited until he had finished speaking.

'Now, that is an example of what I was talking about. If you allow your voice to tail off like that, I should have to retreat to the back wall of the court. The alternative is for me to *tell* you to speak up which I never like to do in front of a jury. Above all, they have to hear a clear, cohesive version of events from you.'

Robertson nodded, still distant.

'Another matter which Mr Dowdall will discuss with you is the question of your wife giving evidence. Even before Cameron had finished the sentence, pain flashed across Robertson's face. 'That is still something worth contemplating, despite your stated opposition to the notion, even at this stage.'

Large hands protruding from formerly white shirt cuffs – now wrinkled and tinged with a grey hue – and enveloped his face as his body convulsed in silent grief; tarnished silver cufflinks, a reminder of happier, more normal times, struggled to take the strain, the little linking chain straining to near breaking point.

Having met and discussed Robertson's case with him before counsel's later involvement, Dowdall felt a closer bond to Robertson than they did. The sight of the client's obvious suffering made him intervene.

'Mr Robertson, what senior counsel is saying to you is that the importance of tomorrow cannot be underestimated. You must do yourself justice in the witness box, and the first stage in that process is clearly telling the jury what happened. We know what you are likely to say because we have talked about it. Beyond that, there is little any of us can do to help. We know how much of an ordeal this is going to be for you and are only giving you the benefit of our experience. We know you will be under great pressure.'

Robertson suddenly sat up. He stared intently at Dowdall who had characteristically removed his glasses and was rubbing his eyes with the outsides of his index fingers and so, unlike the other two, was initially oblivious to the rapid alteration in Robertson's expression and bearing.

With the prospect of being heeded properly, Cameron took over again, just as Dowdall replaced the oversized frames on his bulbous nose.

'Mr Robertson, what Mr Dowdall has just told you is of vital importance. You must concentrate as you have never done before when answering both my questions and those of the Advocate Depute.'

Whatever had happened, the accused man at least seemed to be listening. Eye contact, always significant in Cameron's book, was now being made.

However, there was a train to catch, and it was time to depart.

'My junior and I will now leave you with your solicitor so you can discuss the question of which defence witnesses should be called on your behalf. Good evening.' Both counsel stood up and left the room.

Trying to sound businesslike to keep Robertson engaged, Dowdall talked about the value of calling both professional witnesses, the forensic pathologist and the consulting engineer. The combination of their conclusions gave the jury an alternative to murder and kept the door open for a less drastic outcome. That, however, depended on how far the door remained ajar following the accused's evidence. He still seemed to have Robertson's attention. Time to bring up the forbidden subject again.

'Now, I know I have mentioned this before, but the question of your wife giving evidence is now a matter of supreme and urgent importance.'

Robertson groaned but Dowdall persevered, raising both hands defensively to shoulder height, palms outward facing.

'Yes, I know she can't add anything to the events of the early hours of the 28th of July, but she can tell the court about other more general matters such as the sort of father you are to the children.'

Dowdall was acutely aware he was sounding like a door-to-door salesman, desperately hoping the householder might conjoin with so much make believe that his sales pitch might be successful. *Buy this and avoid the rope! It's on special offer!*

Giving advice to a client on how to make him save his own life was a bitter satire, an intuitive absurdity that could only really be justified if it worked, something to be reminisced upon well after the event at a social gathering or a chance street meeting with a revitalised, liberated ex-client.

Salesman's foot now firmly wedged in the door jamb, he continued.

'Above all else, the jury will be able to see for themselves she forgives you! At this moment in time, you may not appreciate it, but that's something that's very important for them to hear.'

Robertson's long stare had returned. He sat upright but mute. As with all conscientious advisers, Dowdall's resolve increased the more it became obvious that his client needed guidance and this was going to take time; having completed the crosswords in both the *Evening Citizen* and the *Evening Times*, the driver of the Barlinnie bus eventually left for its pitiless environs minus one prisoner, instead arranging for a special car to transport Robertson there at the end of the discussion with his lawyer.

Just after half past six, the turnkey who had assured Dowdall that he could take his time was regretting his words. He began jangling the loop of keys, noisily rearranging chairs and whistling loudly. Inside the room, the solicitor was determined to shake his client out of the listless stupor he had seemingly sunk into. There were signs he was getting through. Robertson kept up with the points he was making and occasionally appeared to agree. Janice was the major problem. The best Robertson could do was to promise to think about calling her as a witness, to be confirmed at nine-thirty the next morning.

Dowdall stepped out of the side door of the building into Clyde Street, the light from within immediately extinguishing as soon as the door was closed and locked from within by one of the court squad. It was a cold, drizzly night, and as he walked westwards towards his office, and the mountain of work he was neglecting in favour of the case of the 'Glasgow Policeman on Trial for the Murder of his Friend', as one headline put it, he felt an unusual, unsettling dissatisfaction with his chosen profession. Demobilisation from the Royal Navy at the end of the war had concentrated his mind and a switch to the less lucrative but more stimulating criminal law had followed. Up until this case it had been a welcome change. As darkly dressed figures in mufflers and Donegal caps came and went out of the gloom in the feeble lights in Clyde Street, some eyeing the possessions of the smartly dressed man with the briefcase as a prospective source of a good night's drinking, Dowdall's mind drifted towards the Gorbals, now just the width of the river away. Life does indeed go on and tonight's tragedies would become tomorrow's court cases, the *dramatis personae* either dead and gone or unwilling leads in the denouement of the play. If only people realised the truth. The truth about what they did to each other. The truth about the untold harm a sudden impulse can cause. Just a few months ago, a child from those gloomy, gaslit streets came into this world. He could have been a scholar or a scoundrel, a saint or a sinner, but then he had a mother to run to when a bully took his pennies or love broke his heart in later life. But she was gone forever in a motorised slalom of tyres and metal, human detritus on the highway of time, ever compelled to keep moving on.

That the child's father *would* be there for him was never

likely to happen.

That he *could* be there for him was another matter and that depended on tomorrow's dramatic events.

Chapter 33

The police court squad were a varied bunch with mixed reactions to the entire legal process. Some were youngsters in their late 20s recovering from illness or injury, some were half-way through their allotted service and had reason to be taken out the front line of policing, and the rest were coasting towards retirement. The job consisted of getting remanded prisoners to and from court on time and keeping order once a trial had started. Two of their number escorted prisoners from downstairs into South Court and another two did the same in the North Court, then sat silently beside them, white gloved and with batons drawn. Should there be any trouble, they were expected to quell disturbances in the public benches, subdue awkward accused and assist witnesses engaged in fainting fits – be they genuine or not.

Most of the court squad's number began their stint indoors deeply cynical about the obvious effort the prosecution took to ensure – and defence counsel demanded – that fairness to the accused was paramount. But that changed over time as they cottoned on to the system and realised juries *usually* came to the right verdicts, particularly in capital cases. Dangerously in possession of only some of the facts of a case, the court squad morphed into surrogate downstairs jurors themselves and the pair assigned to dock escort duty in the Robertson trial were debriefed by colleagues every day around five o'clock. Since the accused, atypically, was one of their own, most started out fervently hoping for a resounding acquittal, views ranging from *it must have been an accident right enough* to *even if he did run her over, they still have to come up with a reason for it.* By the end of the Crown case though, the ranks of those who preferred the 'accident' theory had dwindled to one or two dreamers who refused to accept their former colleague's guilt under any circumstance, whereas the more realistic, more logical *alright then, was being a demanding nuisance a good enough reason to commit vicious, pitiless murder?* faction was winning the five o' clock debate downstairs.

Of course, in light of what they had heard up till now, to achieve an outcome favourable to Robertson, the jury would probably have to return a verdict with no basis in logic or even in the evidence they had heard with their own ears – a verdict which said *he did it alright but we don't see the sense in killing him as well so we made believe the reason wasn't good enough.* A majority Not Proven would suffice. A unanimous culpable homicide with no possible earthly basis in any one of the Crown witnesses' testimonies would do just as well. Then he could go home to his nice little wife and kids and become something of a notorious celebrity car salesman or go back to making engines for Rolls Royce, *but have an affair with him then try to blackmail him at your peril.*

All that was needed now was the foundation for the fib, a fictitious excuse for leniency and we can all go home wiser and he can get on with it, a chastened man, wary about lowering his trouser zip away from home unless for good pressing, diuretic reasons.

Above all though, never *ever* try to blatantly con or dupe the jury in your bid for freedom, as you are all now part of the same team. If you do, they will punish you for not meeting them at least halfway on the road of crafted pretence, them waiting at the illusory gates of freedom and you meeting them there without the key.

That morning, Dowdall went to the Saltmarket from his office, having cleared some of the backlog of work the night before. Working into the small hours, followed by a sleepless night and an early start, yet with no thoughts of tiredness or fatigue, the rush of anxiety, dread and hopefulness commingling gave him the drive to see the landmark day through. At times like these, clients were more than clients. They were troubled fellow humans badly needing help and support. Given their chance in the witness box, some, of course, spurned their big moment in the spotlight or embellished outlandishly, giving their counsel an empty, standardised speech at the end, going through the motions of seeking justice for an evidently culpable man. Cameron's doggedness had got the client this far and Dowdall now needed to know if Janice was to be called. Beyond that, the question was whether a snatched five minutes in the cells with him would help or hinder his ability to do himself justice, whatever that might mean in the final reckoning.

The Macer appeared as soon as Dowdall placed his briefcase on the ancient Gown Room wake table to tell him the word from the cells was that his client needed to speak to him.

Not wanted, *needed*.

Once his coat, hat and scarf were safely draped on the mahogany coatstand, he declined his first cup of tea and made his way downstairs, assuming Robertson had seen sense at the last minute and was wanting to confirm that his wife should give evidence and narrow the options for the jury even further in his favour.

Sitting at the vandalised table again, he noticed they were back to two chairs, one either side. Perhaps the case in the South Court must be using more valuable resources than the traditionally more serious ones heard in the North, he mused as Robertson's steady tread could be heard making its way along the dimly lit corridor, competing with the continual rattle of chains and keys from the turnkey.

Robertson's demeanour immediately sparked hope in Dowdall's heart; perhaps his coming weekend might not be plagued with thoughts of impending catastrophe after all.

Robertson had changed his shirt and was wearing a thin azure-blue coloured tie which snaked evenly down to his leather-belted waist, emphasising his broad shoulders as well as the clearly defined lines of a different, previously unseen charcoal grey suit. He was smiling. What a difference it made to him, from darkness to daylight, from a gloomy winter's day to a warm August afternoon, his grin flashing those healthy white teeth just beneath an Errol Flynn pencil of thin, well-trimmed upper lip hair.

As the turnkey made for the door on the way out of the room, he turned, smiled at Dowdall and nodded his head sideways in the prisoner's direction in a silent gesture of *Get him! He's in a good mood today!* just as Robertson extended a long strong arm to shake Dowdall's hand for only the second time since they had met. The door closed; Dowdall sat back on the creaking chair expecting good news. Sometimes the days you dread in advance turn out for the best.

'So, Mr Robertson, I'm glad to say you seem to be in a much better frame of mind since we spoke last night.'

'I am indeed, Mr Dowdall, I am indeed.' He looked and sounded almost euphoric.

'I take it you've come to a decision about calling your wife to give evidence on your behalf then,' Dowdall said confidently.

'I have, Mr Dowdall. I did a lot of deep thinking last night about all you said.'

Dowdall began to write the anticipated last-minute instructions on the familiar yellow notepad as he spoke.

Still smiling, Robertson spoke in the loud, confident voice that senior counsel had advised. 'And I firmly believe that the right thing to do is *not* to call her.'

Dowdall stopped writing and looked up at the other man who was clearly happy about his decision. Not just any decision, but one that could cost him his life. It got worse. Still smiling, he emphasised his words by tapping the table with his right index finger.

'And something else, I'm going to refuse to admit there was anything going on between the Murphy woman and me. She was just someone I knew in the course of my work, like many folk you meet every day when you are out on the beat.'

Dowdall put his pen down. There was no point in writing any more of his client's words. They ran counter to all the advice he had given him and to all this client had said before at consultation. It now became imperative to discuss matters before it was too late, which would be in less than an hour's time.

Dowdall's pulse raced as he contemplated the probable effect of these latest instructions. 'Mr Robertson, might I remind you what you told me when I came to see you in Barlinnie for the second time? You accepted that there was something going on between you and Miss Murphy. Changing your instructions at this late stage will cause difficulties for counsel. All the evidence about you being the father of her second child went virtually unchallenged except for when it was said he had his father's hair colouring, and Mr Cameron pointed out that the child has reddish colouring and your hair is black.'

If anything, Robertson's smile had widened.

'I make no apology for this. If it means you cannot continue to act for me, so be it.' He had made up his mind and there was to be no going back.

Dowdall sat in silence, weighing up what the right thing to do might be. Neither he nor Cameron were the sort to walk away from someone in need, the need in this case being as extreme as could be imagined, but this verged on idiocy on the client's part. Counsel might justifiably withdraw from acting now that an important part of the defence case had been changed at the last minute. It was obvious to everyone in court what had been going on between the prisoner and the deceased and counsel could have taken account of that in his speech, reminding the jury they were in a court of law, not a court of morals, the canard that hints at it being alright to overlook good old-fashioned motive to arrive at a rope-evading verdict. Now he couldn't.

He picked up his fountain pen and started writing again.

The Saltmarket
Friday 10th November 1950

I, James Ronald Robertson, hereby instruct my solicitor and counsel representing me in the current trial in which I am charged with the murder of Katie Murphy, not to call my wife Janice Robertson as a witness on my behalf. I further instruct my counsel to proceed on the basis that there was never any impropriety between the deceased woman and myself, she being someone who lived in the area which I patrolled and that I only knew her as a passing acquaintance.

Signed –

Once he finished writing, Dowdall turned the pad round and suggested the client read through then sign where indicated if the terms were correct. As Robertson read it over, Dowdall hoped he might have a change of heart and climb down from the impossibly moralistic straitjacket he was about to impose on his defence team.

What then happened was the exact opposite of what he wished for – Robertson appended his signature with a flourish before turning the pad back round. He then carefully replaced the cap on the pen and placed it on the desk beside the pad. It was a final gesture signifying there would be no more discussion about it.

Dowdall collected them up, still stunned at how definite Robertson appeared to be in coming to such a momentous decision, one which would have such obviously prejudicial repercussions.

As he stood up to leave, Robertson tried to break the ice which had rapidly formed between them.

'I honestly appreciate all that you and counsel have done for me, but I am never going to admit in public that I let my family down in any way. How could they attend church on a Sunday knowing I had slipped from the standards I myself demanded they achieve themselves?'

Dowdall sat down again, hope springing only briefly. Was he wanting to be persuaded from this stubborn, dangerous path? One last try. Maybe some shock tactics might make him see sense so that it could all be written off as last-minute nerves then the recently signed page can be torn up.

'Mr Robertson, I can only speak for myself, but I should imagine your wife and children would prefer you were still with them when they next attend Sunday worship. In my view, your insistence that your wife is not to be called on your behalf and your change of instructions have combined to drastically reduce your chances of *ever* seeing the inside of your church hall again!'

If that didn't do it, nothing would.

His words had absolutely no effect on the client, who simply stood up – still smiling, and apparently content with his unwavering certitude.

'So be it,' he said softly as he made his way towards the door, automatically extending both wrists towards the turnkey lest he should see the need to cuff him for the short 30-foot journey to the holding cell.

Dowdall looked at his watch. 9.50a.m. The court would be sitting in ten minutes, and he still had to let counsel know about this inexplicable turn of events. Who knows? Maybe the imperturbable Jock Cameron would withdraw from acting as some counsel certainly would, giving them a cast iron excuse for taking the next train east and return to money making ventures again, writing the Robertson fiasco off to experience, all the while suppressing a gnawing, unsettling feeling that more could have been done to prevent a man going to the gallows.

By the time Dowdall made it back to the Gown Room, both senior and junior counsel were dressed for court, the junior collecting up their papers from the wake table and about to make the short journey to the North Court. Dowdall halted their progress by standing in the doorway.

'Gentlemen, there may be a slight delay in proceedings starting this morning. I have just spoken to the client and certain complications have arisen.' Both counsel returned to the table and sat down as Dowdall explained the change in circumstances, pushing the recently signed precognition pad towards them to confirm the client's incomprehensible perversity.

Cameron read it over impassively then told his junior to go to the courtroom and tell the clerk and the macer that there might be a short delay in starting that morning's proceedings. Then he sat back, rested the back of his left hand on his chin and factored this latest mystifying news into the complicated pools and eddies of the evidential pond. After a few minutes, the junior returned to say the judge had been told and he was prepared to allow 'a ten-minute hiatus' to proceedings and if anything longer was needed, he would have to be addressed without the presence of the jury.

Cameron pondered for a further minute, then pushed the pad back towards Dowdall, who was becoming anxious about his senior's continued involvement in the case of His Majesty's Advocate against James Ronald Robertson. At last, Cameron spoke.

'Well, Laurence, you know this man better than I do, so it would be pointless for me to make a gratuitous observation here. He does of course realise that he will alienate the jury and Leslie will tear him to shreds in cross now, doesn't he?'

It looked like Cameron was prepared to carry on acting for the client. Relieved, Dowdall replied, 'He does, and what's more curious is that he seems very happy about it. I realise this is going to cause you a lot of bother and I was worried in case you thought this latest twist might force your withdrawal.'

'Some might, but I see it as my duty to persevere and take this to the end.' A rare smile creased his stony features. 'The trouble with this occupation can be summed up in one word: clients! It's not the first time I've had to be more nimble-footed that I thought I was capable of, but we can soldier on. One last thing though. He is aware he is committing suicide in a very public forum, isn't he?'

Chapter 34

Whenever the system of trial by jury comes under attack – usually from disappointed parties whose interests have been thwarted – supporters rush to its defence, coming away with medieval sounding pronouncements that they are 'the golden thread of justice' or 'the bulwark against tyranny', when the evidence often shows something entirely different. Once jurors realise they are all powerful when it comes to the facts of every case, they are free to indulge whatever emotion or prejudice their collective will allows, sometimes completely contrary to the story witnesses have told in court. Once naturally inclined to like an accused or feel sorry for him, it often takes an overwhelming Crown case for them to convict, cynical court personnel correctly predicting acquittals where an accused is an obvious underdog.

It has to be said that as a policeman, Robertson got off to a bad start with a jury of Glaswegians, some naturally inclined to convict *before* any evidence had been heard, whilst an important minority of their number at least attempted to be fair.

That a serving policeman was driving a stolen car came as a bit of a shock, either reinforcing or destroying previously held images of a policeman's role and the inherent honesty of the force. After that, the theft of the radio and the logbooks following a break-in at a garage on his beat came as less of a surprise, the mould of trust already broken into small, unfixable pieces. But that was not why they were there, in the High Court, bad as the outrageous abuse of office clearly was. Katie's murder had to be seen as another dimension, a descent into depravity and evil that only some amongst us could be capable of, regardless of what it takes for a policeman to steal. Initially, on hearing the desperate

201

situation she was in, it was easy to assume any sympathy went her way, which it must have, but the turning point of every trial can be when the defence case begins and the flow of compassion sometimes reverses. Should he decide to give evidence, the accused is usually obliged to speak first, all eyes studying him and testing his words, but even if he fails to impress, chances to redeem his shortcomings still exist with other, later witnesses.

That morning, Robertson looked like his moment had come. The oath to tell the truth, the whole truth and nothing but the truth was repeated in a steady, clear, loud voice, his right hand extended high above his sharp centre parting, causing his jacket to pull to one side to reveal sharply creased suit trousers.

Yes, he was married and had two children. Yes, he knew the Austin 16 DYS 570 was really CVD 350 because he had put the false plates on it himself and no, he had not stolen it. Well, not quite. He had seen it parked on waste ground near his house, found out it had been stolen in the town centre and had decided to use it himself, but only for a short while, then he would put the original plates back on and dump it somewhere, no harm done. Well, no great harm anyway.

The logbook was one of the ones he found on his beat, and he simply used it to suit his needs. No, he had not broken into a garage on his beat to steal anything. Fair enough. That could happen to a beat cop, out at night when no one's about, finding things a thief has dropped in his haste to get home. So far, no great injury to common sense, just unease about the car thing and the dodgy plates.

Cameron's experience played its part, his questions sounding unimpeachably direct and incisive.

'You were driving the Austin on the night of the 27th and into the morning of the 28th of July last. Do you accept that?'

'I do, sir.'

'You were driving that vehicle on Prospecthill Road, Glasgow just after midnight on the latter date. Do you accept that?'

'Again, sir, I do.'

'Was anyone with you in that vehicle at that time?'

The accused man looked suitably thoughtful. 'Yes, sir, the deceased woman was in the front passenger seat at that time.'

Even to his legal team, the answer sounded a bit cold and impersonal. The blatant weak spot of the defence case – he couldn't have cared less for her. Nothing for it but for Cameron to brazen it out now, even if the client had handicapped their task by his unrealistic, last-minute instructions.

Acutely aware they were both being studied by a now very attentive jury, he took a long, studied look at the accused man, then asked the all-important question.

'Tell the jury how well you knew her.' If a client is hellbent on self-destruction, there are strict limits to what counsel can do. It was better the question came from deliberately badly aimed friendly fire.

With all eyes on him, Robertson's half-hearted effort at lying did him no favours. He was unconvincing. It sounded as if he didn't even believe it himself, the volume of his voice decreasing during the few seconds from the start to the finish of his answer.

'She was someone I knew from beat number eight. She lived there. That was all.'

Because one or two of the jury had already stopped taking notes, they noticed the prosecutor writing the answer down then ostentatiously underlining it several times before placing his pen on the table and adjusting his wig as if readying for verbal combat with the witness. Cameron carried on, outwardly pretending that a flow of satisfactory responses to all his probing questions was in progress. Even he had to put a show on at times.

'Why did you drive to Prospecthill Road?'

A chance for the client to ramble. It was up to him to try to sound credible. Who knows – maybe he would improve the more he spoke?

'Miss Murphy wanted me to drive her further afield, to Neilston, but I decided I had gone far enough because I was on duty.' He hadn't made things better. If anything, he had made them worse. Did he really just say that? *Miss* Murphy? That needed correcting.

'Miss Murphy?' Cameron was publicly signposting the lowest acceptable standard of respect the jury might reasonably expect from the man accused of killing her.

'Yes. Her first name was Katie.' The client caught on, or seemed to.

'Thank you. Anyway, what occurred there?'

Robertson described how an argument developed over her wanting to go further afield and him wanting to get back to his beat to start his shift. She had been acting strangely and was giggling like a girl and she eventually got out of the car so he could get back to the Gorbals. After travelling a short distance – maybe a hundred yards or so – he realised she might be upset so he had a change of heart and reversed back to where he estimated she had been standing. He felt a jarring bump, then stopped the car and stepped out to see her lifeless face peering up at him from beneath the offside running board. He described the panic and the frantic attempts to free her; reverse gear then first gear to try to free the lifeless body now somehow inextricably stuck to the chassis or the driveshaft underneath. Eventually, going slowly forward in first gear, a slight upwards bump lifted the car and told him she had finally become disentangled. He was now free to get back to his beat, to catch up on neglected duties, but the first thing he had to attend to was a broken exhaust. Here he was, driving a car he had no right to be behind the wheel of, absent from his beat, in a state of horror about what had just happened, and the car was attracting attention by the aeroplane sound it was making. He had no alternative but to crawl underneath it and tie the silencer up with rope then take it back to the vacant garage in Salisbury Street, which he did before joining PC Morison on the beat.

Dowdall was keenly conscious of the small but important differences in Robertson's story – not that the jury would know about them. It's always a bad sign when a client's story changes from what he said at consultation to his evidence at the trial, from laying the foundations of the defence case to the cold public scrutiny of the witness box. When it happens, lead counsel's reaction is crucial. A show of surprise at an unexpected answer can alert the opposing team, the judge and most importantly, the 15 judges of the facts – should they notice that something has been altered and they would wonder why. Clients going on unexpected verbal excursions which have never been explored with his legal team lead to opponents investigating suspicious areas of his evidence, if they sensed them. Should they pick up on anything he said coming as a surprise to his counsel, they have to ask what made him change his story if he's being truthful?

Dowdall surreptitiously consulted his notes of their second consultation – the one where he confronted him with some of the awkward facts he had readily discovered after their first meeting. Yet, here he was now, when it really mattered, adapting his version of events. Was it to paint his actions in a better light?

If the accused is seen moving the goalposts at this late stage, it highlights the weakness of his story and can lose him the game shortly after kick-off. What was it Burns said? That's it – *facts are chiels that winna ding*. They are nuggets of hard-boiled truth which can't be broken down or altered in any way. Did Robertson not tell me he *pushed* her out the car by the shoulder but now he's saying she simply got out? Yes, there it is. That's exactly what he said to me in Barlinnie. Another thing. He just told the court he'd driven off and travelled about *one* hundred yards before he regretted leaving her on the pavement, but he previously told me he'd gone about *300 yards* before he reversed back to where he'd left her. What was the point of that? Was it in case he gets asked if it didn't make more sense to turn the car round rather than reverse all that way back? Alright, what difference does it make – a push on the shoulder or driving a couple of hundred yards more than he said on oath? You'd think that five years on the beat and several court appearances giving evidence should at least prepare him for getting small details and estimates of distance right!

I've never really trusted what Robertson has told me about this case. Ok, it's not my job to doubt him or judge him, that's for the jury alone. He acts like he's above all this and that this whole thing doesn't really matter. Still, Jock Cameron's a brick. Thank goodness I got him to do this – all for the cost of exactly zero to either the client or the public purse! Of the pair of them, Jock's the one who should be rewarded in heaven ...

All in all, despite the obvious cold-heartedness of his behaviour, the examination in chief had picked up slightly. Some of the jury appeared *reasonably* content with what he had said. Usually a good sign, a few of the women took some time to finish writing and once finished seemed relieved that the burden of the task awaiting them at the end of the case had been eased.

At that stage in the trial, the whole ghastly episode added up to an unfortunate, irretrievable accident, but the Advocate Depute still had to ask the accused man some questions. Despite showily underlining obvious areas of attack in his note of Robertson's evidence, Harald Leslie was not one for eye-catching gestures or dramatic acts. Robertson stood easy in the witness box looking relaxed as Leslie made his way to the lectern. Choosing the *let's get some things out of the way* approach in his distinctive Orcadian inflection, he confirmed a few recently made admissions mainly for the jury's benefit.

'So, you accept that you *were* present in Prospecthill Road, Glasgow on 28th July when Katie Murphy died?'

'I was.'

'Was anyone else there or was it just the two of you?'

'No, there was no one else there.'

'You drove a car over her, did you not?'

'Yes, I did drive a car over her.' Watched intently by Dowdall, Robertson came across as relaxed and appropriate at this early stage of what would undoubtedly be a gruelling examination. *Never underestimate an opponent because he doesn't sound aggressive.*

'You moved the car backwards and forwards over her, did you not?' The prosecutor sounded very calm and relaxed, as if he might be chatting to a neighbour across the garden fence somewhere in the New Town.

'No, I did not.'

'You did not?' He sounded surprised. 'Did you not just tell this court you did?'

'No, not backwards *and* forwards. What I said was that the car accidentally went over her as I was reversing it.' Robertson's confidence from his examination in chief had spilled over. How long would it last, or be allowed to last?

Leslie stroked his chin, thinking deeply about the questions to come.

'I'm not sure I understand what you mean. Did you not say that you put the vehicle in first gear and moved it forward *after* you realised she was underneath it?'

'I did. That was in an effort to disentangle her from the car.'

'Alright. According to you, the car struck her accidentally

as you reversed it towards where she had been standing on the kerb, causing her to fall onto the roadway and go under the wheels?'

'That is what happened.'

'Can you explain why you drove it forward?'

'To try to get her free of the driveshaft or whatever it was that was stopping her from me pulling her out from underneath.'

'So, you drove forward?'

'I did.'

'And over her body?'

'Yes, I did, so that I could get her out from underneath.'

'You must have realised she would have been injured a second time when you did that?'

The accused man's legal team seemed unfussed, apparently noting the evidence normally, but covertly worried what their client's response was going to be. Either way, it was going to amount to a callous attempt to flee the scene regardless of whether she still had a spark of life in her or not.

Robertson's brow was beginning to furrow with anxiety. 'I knew that. I've seen many dead bodies since I joined the Glasgow Police and knew she was beyond help as soon as I saw her under the running board.'

'So, you personally pronounced her dead then drove over her again so you could leave the scene?' Leslie was starting to tighten the screw, yet his voice lacked aggression.

'If you want to put it like that.' Robertson was still defiant in his answers.

'What effort did you make to free her before you took the drastic action of driving forwards?'

'I got down on my knees and pushed and pulled her by the shoulders, but she was firmly stuck.'

Leslie weighed up his next point, allowing a faint, sceptical *hmm* to escape from his mouth as he did so. 'How hard did you try to untangle her?'

'I tried really hard to get her out. I reached underneath and pulled at her clothes and her legs, but it was no use.'

'I see,' Leslie said, reeling him in for the next attack on his account of events. 'Do you recall the evidence of Professor Glaister?'

'I do, sir.'

'Do you recall the evidence of Police Constable Kevan?'

'I do, sir.'

'Is it your position that you struggled to free that unfortunate woman in the manner you have described – and in an area saturated with her blood – yet you managed to do that without your tunic coming into contact with any of her blood?'

'That must be the case,' Robertson said hesitantly.

'The alternative might be that you simply drove away after she had been crushed under the vehicle's wheels, might it not? Leslie's accent and slight speech impediment made his pronunciation of the word 'crushed' – *kwusshed* - sound especially barbaric.

'No, sir, that is not what happened.' By comparison, Robertson's answer sounded flat and unfeeling.

'Alright, if what had happened was purely accidental, why did you not wait until another vehicle appeared and get some assistance in retrieving her?'

'I'm afraid I panicked and just wanted to get away.'

Dowdall noticed Robertson's voice was starting to fade so that some jurors were obviously not hearing all he said – usually the sign of an accused or a witness avoiding awkward questions. The prosecutor leafed through his notes, letting the impact of his questioning settle, fully aware some answers might not have been picked up by all of those who mattered.

Then a rare intervention by the judge.

'Advocate Depute, it appears that some members of the

jury were unable to hear what the panel's last answer was. Perhaps you might ask the question again and perhaps the panel might speak up a bit in response.'

Perfect for the Crown. An area which showed the client in a poor light, to say the least, was being unintentionally bolstered by the bench.

The prosecutor walked to the table and consulted with his junior, clarifying exactly what the answer had been before he resumed his position at the lectern. Robertson was beginning to lean forward in the witness box, his hands now limply clasping the wooden frame, his shoulders drooping and rounded.

'Can you confirm to the court that in response to me asking you why you did not seek help to recover the body of Katie Murphy from under the wheels of the car, you answered "I'm afraid I panicked and just wanted to get away". Is that correct?'

'Yes'. His voice had risen again, reinforcing his pitiless actions.

'Can you also confirm that you told your counsel the silencer had become detached and that you stopped, I think, in Cumberland Street to effect a temporary repair using rope you carried in the vehicle's boot?'

'I did.'

'How did you attach the rope to the exhaust system?'

'I crawled underneath the car.'

'In Cumberland Street?'

'Yes, that was in Cumberland Street.'

'Could you not have crawled underneath the car in Prospecthill Road to free the trapped woman?'

The prosecutor's tactic of returning to certain weak points in the defence case was having the desired effect and Robertson's words were beginning to have an *ad hoc*, concocted ring to them.

'I suppose I could have … well, maybe not, no, there

wasn't enough room to do that.' The answer had all the hallmarks of made up lies, fabricated to fit the occasion.

Leslie unhurriedly flicked through his notes, court time moving at a snail's pace now working in the Crown's favour and against the man who always must have known he would one day have to account for his actions that summer's morning. That moment had come, so why find the easy questions so hard? Tougher ones were still to come.

'Explain again how it was you came to meet the deceased woman on the night of the 27th?'

'I saw her by chance in Cavendish Street when I was taking the car to park it.'

'By chance?'

'That's correct.'

'There could be no suggestion of an arrangement to meet her at that time and at that place, could there?'

'No, none at all.' He tried to sound firm and confident, but his voice wavered slightly. Some of the women on the jury had a faraway look in their eyes, as if they knew they were now going to have to contemplate the unthinkable and convict this faltering man of capital murder.

'Do you recall the testimony of the lady from the National Assistance Board?'

Given the jury's reaction to her overbearing manner, Robertson seemed to imagine he could turn this to his advantage. He forced a brief smile before he spoke.

'Of course I do!'

Dowdall quickly checked the jurors' reactions. None of them registered anything other than concentrated recall – certainly no shared amusement.

The prosecutor briefly consulted the Crown junior's handwritten notes. 'And do you recall her telling this court that the weekly allowance for children is subject to a statutory reduction in the event of the mother failing to disclose the identity of the child's father?'

It dawned on Robertson where the Advocate Depute was going with this line. He murmured a simple 'Yes'.

'And do you recall her telling this court that the claim made by the deceased woman Miss Murphy on behalf of the child Andrew, born at 6.37a.m. in the morning of the 22nd of April 1950 at the maternity hospital, Glasgow, was so abated for that reason? In other words, she refused to divulge the identity of the child's father.'

Another mumbled 'Yes.'

'Tell me, Mr Robertson, is it true that, up until Miss Murphy's death, you were in the habit of paying regular weekly sums to her of approximately ten shillings per week?'

Another weak response, this time an unconvincing 'No.'

Leslie closed one folder over as if that chapter had been dealt with then picked another one up. The jury could see 'theft of motor vehicle' and 'break-in at garage' written in large letters on it by some admin assistant during case preparation. Dowdall managed a surreptitious glance in Leslie's direction, noticing the change in tempo and hoping the Crown had finished with exploring the exact nature of his client's relationship with the dead woman. Cameron betrayed no emotion, having recognised a ploy he himself had certainly used before. Move on, cover a few anodyne matters, then return with a vengeance to the main issue.

'Tell the court, if you will, how it was you came to find out how the Austin 16 had been stolen, unless you yourself actually took it from West Campbell Street in Glasgow in May of this year.'

Imagining he had endured and survived the awkward chapter of evidence, Robertson relaxed and once more assumed an erect stance, placing his hands behind his back and pushing his barrel chest forward.

'I noticed the car parked near to my house in the Cardonald area of the city and stupidly thought I could use it for a while. I never intended to keep it, only run it for a few weeks.'

'It did not belong to you and never had?'

'That's right.'

'So, you stole it?'

'I suppose so.'

For the first time, Leslie's voice rose slightly as if he was losing patience. 'There can be no "suppose" about it, Mr Robertson. You either stole it or you didn't.'

Relieved that the prosecutor seemed to be concentrating his fire away from more delicate areas, Robertson chanced another smile before he spoke. A few of the jury subconsciously mirrored it, the sides of their mouths involuntarily creasing upwards. *They're still with him!* Dowdall thought. *Despite everything, some of them are still with him!*

'Yes, I stole it – but not from the city centre.'

'And you affixed false registration plates to it, did you not?'

'I did, yes.'

'And you completed a stolen logbook in the new identity you gave the car, did you not?'

'I did, yes.' Robertson imagined he was on the home straight, looking directly towards the jury, some of whom still looked away rather than meeting his gaze. Dowdall continued writing, inside thinking *For God's sake, don't overdo it!*

'Where did the logbook come from?'

'I found it in a back court in Salisbury Street along with other blank ones and a car radio.'

'And was it then you decided to fill it in yourself and keep the car?'

'That's correct.'

'In order to disguise the fact you were driving a car that did not belong to you, did you make up stories about who the car belonged to? For instance, did you not tell Chief Inspector Dougall the car belonged to a friend who had given you a loan of it and others it belonged to your brother who was working abroad?'

'I did.'

'So, you freely admit you are capable of telling lies to colleagues and senior officers to avoid them discovering the truth?'

'If you want, yes.' The answer sounded a bit too flippant for his lawyers' liking.

'Mr Robertson, it's not what *I* want, it's a simple matter of the truth. You are the sort of person who is capable of telling lies to get himself out of a tight spot. That is the case, isn't it?'

Robertson had gone quiet again, mumbling, 'Yes' and slouching forward once more, his hands were now gripping the edge of the witness box.

'Tell the court about the entry in the log held in the Cumberland Street police box at 02.10 hours on 28th July 1950. That was made by you, was it not?'

Another mumbled 'Yes.'

Leslie read it over silently before he spoke, adding over a minute to the accused's public torment.

'You wrote:

'At 12.50 today, a woman was knocked down and fatally injured in Prospecthill Road. The motor car, believed to be a small blue Austin, maybe about ten-horsepower, was driven by a man wearing a light brown Burberry coat. The car did not stop and was last seen driving citywards on Aikenhead Road.'

Firstly, can you say where that information came from?'

As when the actual entry had been made, Robertson was now saturated with sweat and desperate.

'I made that up,' he said in a small, hoarse voice.

Leslie edged towards the witness box; his head turned

214

slightly to the jury.

'I'm sorry, I'm not sure any of the jury heard your answer. I certainly didn't. Repeat it please.'

'I made that up!' The answer was almost shouted. Jurors looked embarrassed for the accused man as he reached into his jacket pocket, produced a handkerchief and began dabbing his forehead, cheeks and neck, his eyes betraying the hope that his humiliation might be at an end.

Leslie replaced the folder on the lectern and reached for the first one again. An ominous sign. Far from nearing its end, the torment was just beginning again.

'Going back to the deceased woman, I would like to further explore the nature of your relationship with her. How well did you know her?'

The accused man almost groaned before he straightened himself up for one last defensive rally, one final effort to repel boarders without weapons using his bare hands. He cleared his throat as he loosened his tie.

'I knew her as well as some of the others who lived on beat eight. She was a passing acquaintance.' The phrase 'passing acquaintance' now sounded contrived, hackneyed and hollow.

Some of the jurors stopped writing and bowed their heads as if out of reverence for a passing funeral procession.

Clinically, Leslie started with the first time Robertson had been called to her house in Nicholson Street, then moved on to the birth of her second child and the local information that the father was a local policeman; the answers sounded empty, the voice devoid of belief and sincerity. By the time the prosecutor had moved on to the night of the 27th into the morning of the 28th, the public spectacle of a once proud married policeman with two young children vainly competing in a one-sided verbal joust to save his life had become almost obscene. His cause was not helped by Robertson glaring at Leslie at one stage through narrowed, hateful eyes, as if he would murder him if he could. Odd then, perhaps, that he was still able to muster enough *animus* to resent being slowly dismantled in cross examination.

There had never been any question that he had had to give evidence. Otherwise, there were too many imponderables needing answers. Now that had happened, there was no question he had to tell the truth and that had clearly *not* happened. Like an unstoppable incoming tide, nothing was overlooked and by the time Leslie was concluding his incisive, almost brutal cross examination the accused man was all but defenceless. Leslie was astute enough to recognise when enough was enough, for the jury's benefit rather than the prisoners. The newborn child, the weekly payments, the 'coincidental' meeting in Salisbury Street, the trip in the stolen Austin, the argument in Prospecthill Road were all explored in detail before the torture was finished.

'And all this for a "passing acquaintance,"' he stated rather than asked. Sounding almost pitying, Leslie's distinctive tones softened to the point of sympathy. He had one final question. 'It is clear, is it not, that you have been untruthful about the actual nature of your relationship with Katie Murphy and that you subdued her before murdering her under the wheels of that stolen car in the early hours of 28th July 1950 in Prospecthill Road, Glasgow?'

The accused man looked helplessly towards his lawyers' side of the table, a child at his parents' feet seeking answers to some of life's bewildering riddles. None of the three looked up, anxious not to be seen to be throwing a lifebelt to a desperate, drowning client.

Without waiting for a reply, Leslie slowly returned to the advocate depute's side of counsels' table, disconsolately threw his case papers onto it and then slumped down into his seat, fully conscious he had added another cross-border appointment to the amiable Albert Pierrepoint's diary. No answer ever came anyway.

Chapter 35

Knowingly fighting a lost cause in court is often bad for team morale, and, barring an unexpected miracle, requires extra reserves of determined spirit. Despite his advisers' resolve, no such marvel was likely to happen in James Ronald Robertson's case, mainly due to the strictures he himself had imposed on his advisers. *Not* calling Janice and *not* admitting paternity made the outcome of the case almost inevitable which in itself, of course, did not stop the trial from continuing.

For the record's sake, Cameron *did* re-examine his client to make sure the court at least heard what turned out to be feeble denials of murderous conduct. He also *did* lead a forensic pathologist and an engineer in an effort to refute the Crown experts' findings, but it was all too late.

Robertson knew that when members of the CID found out that a suspect's alibi was false, they automatically assumed his guilt. As he'd told senseless lies about the true nature of his relationship with Katie, Robertson ruled out any chance of the jury accepting his account of anything after that. Contempt of intelligence can have greater consequence than contempt of court.

Treat us like this and you will pay the price – you deserve to.

The speeches were later described as *forensic jewel oratory* by Dowdall – a lawyer's praise, but cold comfort for a client in a capital case. For the Crown, there is never a case where it's right to *demand* a conviction. An expert in restrained and respectful understatement, the prosecutor succinctly let the evidence do the talking when he said 'I feel it incumbent on me to submit that there was a bond between the two which the woman was maintaining, and which he was seeking to break.' It was almost charming the way he phrased it.

For the defence, Cameron's speech lasted two and a half hours, in the course of which he reminded the jury of the thankless task ahead of them. 'You hold a set of scales. On the right there is a human life, Robertson's. On the left is the evidence – theory, surmise, or suspicion will not do.'

On being invited to retire and consider their verdicts, the unlucky jurors trooped towards their jury room to carry out their sworn duty, some downcast with their burden. Not one of their number looked up from their short trek out of the courtroom to the jury room, and there was no nervous whispered chatter as they left.

Robertson was led silently downstairs by two dock escorts, who were keenly aware they would probably not be releasing their prisoner to his family that night.

Cameron, Kissen and Dowdall sipped tea and coffee in the Gown Room in silently reflecting on how different things might have turned out. Leslie chose to remain upstairs watching the Clyde drift murkily by rather than follow the unspoken convention of joining the defence team for tea in polite but pointless speculation about the outcome of the case. Dowdall did his best to convince himself that postponing his visit to the cells downstairs was the right thing to do for the client's sake, and not just for his own peace of mind. He had previously made his way into an almost deserted defence witness waiting room and told a dejected and lonely looking Janice to go home and stand by the phone, rather than possibly spend tortured hours waiting around, particularly as her husband had steadfastly refused to see her at any time and in any circumstances from the day he had been arrested. Anyway, in capital cases, juries always take ages to decide a man's fate. *Don't they?*

Not this time.

After only 63 minutes, the buzzer sounded. *63 minutes!*

Barely sufficient time for a gentleman to settle his hotel bill! as Shaw, whose death had been reported the week before, had once said in a different context.

The court assembled. There was no unseemly scramble by relatives as the public benches were only half full, a final snub to the memory of Katie Murphy, like unwanted funeral programmes lying scattered on pews at the end of a memorial service. In contrast, the press benches were crammed, a verdict of guilty in a capital murder against a serving policeman being uniquely newsworthy. *This will sell some copy! Fingers crossed he gets done!*

Cameron was uncharacteristically tense – not that he would ever admit to it. It took a different brand of courage to see this sort of thing through. Not the sort that earned him the Distinguished Service Order during the last war; his own death in combat would have been a sudden happenstance, a possibility, maybe even a probability at Dunkirk or Normandy – not this slow, mechanical, grinding process the state favoured when exterminating one of its wayward citizens.

Dowdall's foreboding intensified as the judge's arrival on the bench was signalled by the Macer's shouted instruction for the court to rise, Lord Keith's sombre expression beyond that of a man now likely to have to condemn another to death. It looked like he *knew* he had to.

It's bad practice to gawp at the jury as they funnel into court and take their allotted seats, but even Cameron turned briefly to catch a passing glimpse of tearful women and beetroot-faced men, one of whom clutched a clipboard which held the key to either three weeks or three decades of continuing life for the man in the dock. For the first time in the trial, the accused man ascended the stairs in the jury's sight from the cells below and now stood poker-straight to attention beside two former colleagues who indulgently stared over at the 15 people who were about to announce their prisoner's fate.

An age seemed to pass before the judge nodded towards the Clerk to ask the spokesman for their verdicts. Meanwhile, his Lordship had checked that the black tricorn was in its allotted pigeonhole on the bench.

The clipboard holder rose to his feet and spoke.

'Charge one, theft of the Austin: guilty by a unanimous verdict.' *Unanimous!* Not even a hint that there might be some truth in him simply coming across the car *after* it had been stolen as he had claimed. Guilty of theft *from where it had been spirited off from* one Saturday night in the town centre as the lawyer car owner and his wife dined nearby and Robertson, presumably out of uniform, sized it up, stole it then magically hid it somewhere before announcing its arrival to friends and family like a new-born foundling.

As if.

'Charge two, break-in and theft – guilty by a unanimous verdict.'

No comfort there either. Not one of their number had any doubts that the accused man had broken into the garage on his beat, this time presumably *in* uniform, to steal blank logbooks to go with his newly acquired urchin Austin.

No mercy so far, which did not augur well for the main charge.

'What is your verdict on charge three?' The Clerk's voice resonated round the tomblike stillness of the North Court, but there was no response as the jury spokesman's voice faltered. Silhouetted in a ray of winter sunshine suddenly appearing through windows high above, he cleared his throat while a woman in the shade beside him began sniffling and dabbing her eyes and nose with a flowery patterned hanky.

'Guilty by a majority,' he eventually croaked, the clipboard now quivering slightly in his shaky grasp. All eyes turned to the statuesque form standing to attention in the dock.

Nothing.

No flicker, no reaction, nothing. Just channelled, forward-facing concentration as if he was on guard duty in a sentry box, or on war time parade being inspected by a dignitary.

It did not take long to record the verdicts and read them back. Leslie then sombrely moved for sentence and the Macer ascended the steps to the bench, retrieved the tricorn from its usual compartment, and held it unsteadily aloft, hovering above the judge's head. He began pronouncing the punishment for murder, setting the date, place and time of death by hanging with the added 'pronounced for doom' lest the prisoner be curiously mindless of his surroundings and his predicament.

Looking at Robertson though, he could have been.

The judge thanked the jury, who stood up and gloomily ambled out of court, the few who had wanted to acquit more ashen faced than tearful.

True to form, having given everything and done all he could for his client, Cameron quickly reverted to the apparently emotionless, Hindenburg-like figure he normally was, and within minutes of going downstairs and shaking the condemned man's hand was hastily collecting his portmanteau and rushing off to try to catch the next Edinburgh train, his junior trudging ten yards behind him carrying both bags. No time for sentiment, no time for reflection, no time for 'I-told-you-so's'. He had to keep going and to urgently return to Parliament House to pick up the threads of neglected civil instructions.

Dowdall knew from the start that it was always going to be his unenviable task to deal with a client now under sentence of death. Once counsel had departed the cramped, white-tiled room, he and the doomed prisoner sat opposite each other at the familiar disfigured table; one wistful and regretful, the other silent but strangely controlled. The disheartened lawyer routinely rhymed off the remaining, narrowed options – appeal against conviction, appeal against sentence, a simple appeal for clemency – but from his lack of reaction, there was little doubt that the client was preoccupied and deaf to his words, almost complacently distant, as if already in another place.

Maybe that's where he wanted to be.

Chapter 36

That cold November night, a spacious, flat-fronted Albion 'City of Glasgow Police' prison transfer vehicle, complete with privacy windows and roof ventilators, was detailed to uplift the sole prisoner from the Saltmarket. Capable of holding ten inmates instead of one, this was not because the City Police were transporting one of their own in preferential style – anyway, it was their diligence that had caught him – but was down to a change in his status from untried to convicted. And condemned.

After all, you can't have other insensitive occupants quizzing a fellow convict going on a journey to their final destination.

How'd ye get on, mate? I got a five, what did you get?

Me? I'm getting hanged in December ...

No luck there then. Aw, never mind. Anyway, want a fag? What's that, you don't smoke? Christ! You're having a bad time with it!

After the verdict, the Saltmarket court squad were subdued and careful in their contact with the ill-fated man in their custody. No time constraints on Dowdall's visit – normally the source of much satisfaction to turnkeys everywhere – and no jangling of keys outside the consultation room door. Certainly, none of the usual jibes such as *You'll be back ya jammy bastard!* to the mysteriously acquitted or *You? You're better off inside! It'll do you good to stay off the drink. You'll get more to eat and your missus only shags other men anyway!* to ten-stretchers.

For some of the most recent court squadders, it was strangely emotional. Firstly, seeing such a misfit in their care, then finding out he did it after all, then escorting him to his own private bus to oblivion. Strictly against the rules, the sergeant had ordered no handcuffs for the short journey from the holding cell to the back door to the yard outside. Not that their newly sentenced charge seemed to notice the change in routine, having failed to automatically offer his wrists as he always did, before meekly following the escort in front of him to the door whilst the one beside him held his suit jacket cuff in a token custody kind of way. This one was too calm to try to do a runner.

The light from within flooded the back yard and the rear of the silent, frost-covered bus as the lead officer made his way to the front of the waiting transport to take care of the paperwork. The prisoner and his pensive guardian stood mutely just inside the back door, the chill night air forming small banks of hoary condensation as it met the warmer atmosphere inside.

Noticing the driver and his assistant deep in conversation, the first officer tapped on the passenger door. The passenger inside finished listening to what his colleague had to say before reaching across to wind the window down.

'Date?' he curtly demanded of the officer outside, obviously already aware of the jury's verdict. It was clearly all the same to them employed on the Barlinnie run. So what if some get ten and some get hanged, they're all guilty.

Handing over the copy warrant, the officer said. '16th December coming.' He waited a moment before adding, 'Death by hanging.'

Admin complete and conversation over, the window went back up, the driver complaining of the cold as he pressed the starter button. On constant short runs from court to prison in winter weather, the vehicle's battery struggled to turn the rapidly cooling engine over until the choke was pulled out and increased the fuel intake. When it finally rumbled into life it settled into a steady, throaty rhythm like some sort of high-powered motorboat marooned on land yet only yards from the river.

That signalled the moment for the prisoner to be brought forward to the rear of the bus. Advancing from the shaft of light at the back door through the clouds of billowing grey carbon monoxide fumes which wafted from the bus's exhaust pipe, the escort pulled at the handle on the van's rear door then locked it in position ready to receive its human cargo.

As that happened, a sudden din erupted from somewhere near the porticoed front of the building. Seeing their target silhouetted in the smoky brightness, a small crowd pressed against the railings and began shouting abuse. They had magically assembled in the Saltmarket having travelled the short distance across the river from the Gorbals and were a mixture of friends and relatives of the murdered woman along with others who never knew her but were keen to make the most of the chance to angrily voice their righteous disgust at Robertson in particular and the whole force in general. The police had expected it and had closed Clyde Street to pedestrians, but as the bus grumbled its way out of the yard and into the roadway, the more agile of the mob ran round to continue their tirade as the vehicle made off towards the gaol. Cries of 'Murdering polis filth!' and 'Die ya dirty bastard!' trailed after the dimly lit rear red dots of the slow-moving vehicle as it sluggishly ground its way through the gears and made its way into the darkening night.

Some of the crowd had even anticipated the route the bus would take and took to loitering in close mouths, leaving discarded used matches and thoroughly smoked dog-ends as evidence of their presence there before running forward to administer gratifying thumps on the bus's side as it trundled northwards with its single rear occupant.

Score settled even if you hadn't ever met the lassie!

More paperwork at the prison, this time the other way round, from bus to main gate, then further admin as the verdict triggered a change in accommodation. Given the lateness of the hour and on behalf of the governor, the senior warder consulted the copy court warrant then authorised Robertson's transfer from solitary confinement to the condemned cell. Consulting the rulebook, he delegated the next task to a colleague. Forming a death watch squad required a sufficient number of tactful volunteers with specific attributes, such as that generation's 'proper moral fibre'. Above all, they needed to be the sort who could continually tend to terrified and haunted individuals who screamed during the night and woke up wreathed in sweat from nightmarish visions of restricted breathing and the hell that awaited them in the hereafter.

Married men were better choices for the death watch squad. They were people who knew how to subtly change an unwelcome topic. Men who had served in the forces and had seen their comrades die in the Bocage of Normandy or the darkened sky over industrial Germany or the murderously freezing waters of the Atlantic in a winter convoy. The sort who can play cards on demand, never squabble about football, can listen to the mental ramblings of a man facing certain doom tomorrow then come back to work the day after the execution and go cheerily about their duties as if nothing had happened in between times.

'What about Philips?' the chief warder asked. 'He seems to fit the bill. Ask him when he comes on backshift.'

Chapter 36 ฿

Perhaps it's because capital punishment allows someone to know exactly where, when, and *how* death awaits them that it horrifies and fascinates the rest of us in equal measure. Worse when you have met and acted for that person in the course of their conviction. Passing on the news that there would be no appeal and no reprieve, and that the law must take its stated course was an unenviable, necessary duty that Dowdall had to undergo that freezing winter's day on December 13th 1950.

As he drove into the prison car park, it occurred to him the executioner's box might already be in the building, having read somewhere that it had become the done thing for the hangman to send it on before him. Was it because Pierrepoint might be recognised by abolitionists on a train or boarding a taxi and they might attack and rob him of the tools of his trade, the leather wrist and leg straps, the white cap, twine, shackle, ruler, tape measure, copper wire, pliers and of course the rope? What *would* happen if the court order for the execution to take place at 8a.m. on 16ʰ December 1950 was not followed to the letter? Would it just be rescheduled, and the client be granted a few days more hell on earth?

As he locked the car it struck Dowdall how badly the trial and its outcome had affected him. *Even now, there might be some as yet unknown hitch which might save this client's life.*

The warders seemed more respectful, reverential almost, when he appeared at the front desk in Barlinnie before being led, softly and silently to 'D' Hall and the execution block. Once there, an officer directed him into an empty 'overflow' condemned cell directly opposite the hanging shed, whilst he made his way to arrange the prisoner's presence for a final consultation. Dowdall stood for a few minutes beside the only furniture in the room – a feldgrau coloured chair – rather than sit on it. Who knows who the last person to use it might have been – Carraher? Lyons? Which one of the corpses mouldering in the yard outside?

Having agreed to 'volunteer' for death watch duties, Philips accompanied Robertson to the meeting, Dowdall hearing his soothing voice as he escorted his prisoner along the grey-green walled corridor. In another place and at another time, they might have been a doctor and patient discussing a minor operation or a dentist explaining why surgery on a troublesome molar was needed, such was the professional sounding concern in his voice. His job, naturally enough, was to make sure there were no silences of any great length and to fill them with anything, anything but *that*.

Philips even shook Dowdall's hand, expressing a misplaced, possibly insincere, gratitude for his attendance that cold, sharp morning before leaving solicitor and client alone together.

'Take your time,' he added as he left, Dowdall repressing thoughts of him tastelessly including 'as long as it's less than three days'.

They were only 30 feet or so from the soon to be used gallows that Pierrepoint would be testing the day after tomorrow, whilst the condemned man was out pointlessly exercising, walking round the yard with two of the death watch squad impossibly tasked with making thoughts and images of the looming nightmare recede.

Robertson was kitted out in the garb of the convicted prisoner, a faded open-necked pink shirt and a loose-fitting, grey flannel suit, and long dark woollen socks. No bedding was to be left in the condemned cell during the day and no shoes or belt were to be worn, all removed lest the inmate use them to cheat the hangman. It occurred to Dowdall that Robertson's temporary prison clothes must have been sized when he first appeared on remand as they were now clearly too big due to his weight loss. *Note to prison bureaucrats – wait until the prisoner's been convicted before allotting his final, made-to-measure-for-somebody-else outfit to him. It's more dignified for all of us.*

Robertson clutched the waistband of the oversized trousers as he had shuffled into the cell, Philips thoughtfully carrying a second chair for this their ultimate consultation, his death watch manners not letting him down. He had given a subdued assurance that 'they wouldn't be bothered' as he backed out like an obsequious waiter, deliberately leaving the cell door wide open.

Robertson showed no signs of fear. If anything, he looked boyishly composed – shy, almost – like an impish pupil caught dodging school and about to face the disapproval of his teacher before his parents were told he had let them down.

Dowdall was briefly thrown, having expected an emotional, repentant client and a poignant farewell meeting and instead getting a mildly penitent schoolboy. The lawyer had been dreading meeting a regretful, rueful client who said 'if only' throughout the meeting. *If only* I'd done what you said. *If only* I'd stuck to the truth. *If only* I'd not tried to con the jury about my affair with Katie. How could he answer any of that? *Oh, it's nothing! Don't worry about it, old chap, they're just going to snap your pig-headed spine because* you *thought you knew better!*

He needn't have worried.

Making good steady eye contact, Robertson began the conversation in an apologetic manner as if *he* had somehow failed his legal advisers. No 'if only's', just apologies.

'I'm sorry I didn't do as you said. If I had, I wouldn't be here now. And you don't have to tell me there will be no reprieve. I know that. Philips is a good person, you know. He's a Congregationalist, like Janice was before we got married. Spiritually misguided but a decent fellow nonetheless.' Surely sectarian point scoring as a jocular, farewell flourish had to be an act?

His mention of Janice seemed to set Robertson's mind drifting, giving Dowdall his first chance to contribute.

'Yes, I've spoken to her on the phone since the verdict. I take it you still are set on not seeing her?'

He gulped and shook his head, unable to speak before he composed himself. 'I really couldn't. I don't want this place to be her last memory of me. It's bad enough she came up the path with the children when Mr Dougall came to the house that day. I couldn't face her then and I can't now. At least I never let her down in public, did I, Mr Dowdall?'

Lawyer's instinct for accuracy set aside, Dowdall had no choice but to agree, despite the price about to be paid by a wilful client.

'No, you didn't let her down,' he lied.

'Or the children. Tell me I didn't let them down either.' He was acting like a needy teenage girl demanding eternal love from a passing boyfriend after a first night kiss. *Of course you never let them down – all you did was murder your lover and then make sure your bastard son was orphaned!*

'Or the children,' Dowdall said wistfully. 'You never let them down either.' Better to say what the doomed man wanted to hear.

To Dowdall's surprise, Robertson's face lit up.

'Yes, that's right, I didn't let them down. No one can say I admitted to anything between that woman and me. The children will be able to look the world in the eye and say "I'm sorry, you must be thinking about another person. Our father was not the man who did any of that."'

The distant look that Dowdall had seen in Robertson's face in the North Court during the trial returned, but the pencil moustache remained horizontal, his upper lip suspended in a faraway smile nobody else could understand. Robertson seemed genuinely uplifted by Dowdall's false assurances, borne of the necessity of telling fibs to a dying man.

'Thank you for those words, Mr Dowdall. I needed to hear them.'

It seemed he did. He continued, a look of genuine satisfaction spreading over his face as he spoke.

'As I said, I know if I had followed the advice you gave me I would not be here, but maybe that's because I had to carry out God's will.'

Dowdall nodded, in lieu of fully understanding what his client meant. It might become clearer if he let him talk. Then – nothing. Silence. Not an awkward empty silence, but a calm, almost spiritual peace during which Robertson sat back in the chair appearing more contented than Dowdall had ever seen him looking during the short time that he'd known him. His large, expressive hands were folded on his lap, the white, sun-deprived skin contrasting with the thick, black hair of his wrists and fingers as they nestled in the folds of the ill-fitting flannel trousers. Dowdall wished he could leave now – the moment that this strange, thieving, murdering, devout believer seemed to have made his peace with the world. He began thinking how he could make an appropriate exit but was wary of condemned cell protocol. An ostentatious glance at his watch, followed by suddenly standing up and announcing other business needed attending to would be crass. What other business could be more vital than this, at least as long as he's still alive? Much better to stay on if it helps maintain the current serene mood and gets him to the finishing line in less than 72 hours' time.

Dowdall needn't have fretted. In his newfound tranquillity, the condemned man had sensed the other's discomfort.

'I'm sorry, Mr Dowdall, you must have lots to do rather than sit here listening to me! Please tell Mr Cameron and Mr Kissen how much I appreciated their efforts. Above all, I'd like to thank you for all you did – and tried to do – for me. I feel as if I've got to know you, much more than just as my lawyer. You're more like a best friend than anything else now.'

He reached forward, his hand extended in a firm, farewell grasp which Dowdall took with mixed feelings. *Is this it? Is there nothing more I can do?* Inside, he knew what the answer was.

Again, Robertson took the lead. 'Mr Philips!' he said in a raised voice aware that the attentive official would be near enough to hear him. Philips appeared seconds later in continued lackey butler mode, enquiring if the meeting was over. Robertson confirmed it was and gestured for Dowdall to leave the cell first, out of respect for all his failed endeavours and unheeded advice.

Stepping outside, Dowdall thought it wrong to linger near the execution chamber and made his way towards the front desk in D Hall.

On the way out though, he looked back to where Robertson and Philips were walking, Robertson slip-sliding in his thick woollen socks and clutching the top of his oversized trousers in his right hand as he spoke and Philips seemingly agreeing to some important point his special prisoner was making, the warder's head nodding and his hands held away from his body, palms upturned as if hoping to catch gnostic wisdom from heaven that could be used to ease the other man's impending reckoning.

Something made Robertson look back towards Dowdall and in a tragi-comic moment the condemned man let go of his waistband to wave, then quickly grasped it again as the trousers threatened to slide uncomfortably downwards, the manoeuvre causing his front stockinged foot to slip forward and Philips catching his arm to steady him. Pathos to bathos.

Make sure his body has no bruises before his big day.

The image was to stay with Dowdall. This complex, wayward husband and father who had crashed and burned so spectacularly, now soon on his way to the gallows because he refused to play the game by the rules of an earthly court of law, looked so much like an awkward, gawky son on his way into school with one of his like-minded clumsy pals, never to come back out. As hair shirts go, hanging by the neck until dead had to be the ultimate in righteous penance. *This occupation could be heart breaking. Note to self: must try harder not to treat clients like wilful children or friends in need.*

That, of course, is alright for those who can actually do it.

Chapter 37

The 16th of December 1950 was an emotional day for many. For those who knew Katie, it was bitter-sweet and unfulfilling but better than no justice at all. Even the daily papers who had trumpeted headlines like *Glasgow Policeman To Hang* and who almost gleefully pointed out that to date he was the only serving police officer in Britain to be executed for a crime committed whilst on duty – if it could be truly said he was on duty in Prospecthill Road that July morning – even they showed respectful consideration after the event, consigning his death to a few side columns, albeit front page ones.

Pierrepoint had been careful that chilly December day working out how best to separate Robertson's second and third cervical vertebrae from each other, a smooth road to eternity beginning with stretching the rope to perfection the day before and getting his sums right. Spying on him through the Judas Hole in the condemned cell, he reckoned the doomed man to have lost weight but still to be around twelve stones with above average neck muscle mass. Already aware of his height at six feet two inches, *The Home Office Table of Drops* recommended a precise five feet eleven and a half inches of hempen cord to ensure a successful, clean hangman's fracture. Aware that Robertson would be able to hear his preparations as he tested the equipment, the hangman nevertheless made an effort to soften the racket he made in his genuine efforts to make the procedure more humane. However, there could be no real escape for the condemned man; the realisation that he would be ushered the few steps between the condemned cell and the gallows just before 8am the next day, and after that, he would swing, sway, convulse then dangle for an hour over a pit of sand in the floor below, placed there to absorb dripping body fluids and any escaping excrement.

Nothing personal though. Albert was a true pro – dignity and speed were his bywords. Ten seconds from pinioning to dangling and dripping was good and never any question of mockingly whispering 'Is Germany Still Calling?' to Lord Haw Haw or wondering if Ruth Ellis would cry and smudge and dampen the inside of the white execution hood. Of course she wouldn't. At times like that, women uncomplicated themselves. They became dirty fighters who faced up to reality, sometimes better than their male counterparts – Nurse Cavell style. For some, it was their fate to give life and, if need be, to die under the wheels of a car on a humid summer's night if that's what it took to live a little, rather than to accept the awful truth – that life can't be lived on dreams alone.

Satisfied with a job well done, the executioner stretched soft kid leather gloves over his fingers and wound a cashmere muffler tightly round his neck in his own burlesque little ceremony. He boarded a cab to Central Station, before travelling South to lead the evening sing songs in his hostelry in Oldham – the strangely named 'Help The Poor Struggler'. Singing *Danny Boy* that very night was easy. For Albert, there could be no recriminations, the hangman despatching enemies of the people as Bomber Command and Enola Gay had just a few short years before. Any mistakes – such as the pointless discovery of post execution innocence – belonged to the others who made the rules. Like all the Nazis he had hanged, Albert was only doing his duty, acting on orders from above. And there were no regrets, just fleeting afterthoughts to cope with.

But he were a big lad that policeman from Glasgow. Seen plenty who weren't ready to go and plenty who were, but never seen anyone so pleased *to have it all ended. Obliged him in eight seconds flat I did. Cap, noose, pin, push, drop, then off to the night shift in the sky to pound beat number eight in Heavenly Paradise Southern Division. Much nicer than the bloody Gorbals!*

Chapter 38

Months later and by arrangement, Janice Robertson came to see Dowdall on a mild spring afternoon. She was wearing a bright blue patterned dress, had lipstick on and had had her rose golden hair done in a fashionable poodle cut. Dowdall had not been looking forward to seeing her but, once again, a difficult meeting was made so much easier by the other's unexpected buoyancy.

Like his last meeting with her husband.

Dowdall's secretary, the discreet and always reliable Evelyn, had been looking out for Janice to appear. By the time Dowdall had gone to the waiting room to bring her through, the women were engaged in one of those female-only whispered dialogues that involved a lot of arm touching, sympathetic nodding and understanding smiles. Recognising the futility of contributing to the display of mutual empathy, he stood mutely by until the women signalled that their softly spoken tête-à-tête was concluded by exchanging best wishes in the form of hopes for the future from Evelyn and seemingly cheerful gratitude from Janice.

Janice took her place in the client's chair and, in time-honoured fashion, Dowdall removed the top of his fountain pen and began noting details of the date and time of the meeting. Unusually, the chair's occupant wasn't an accused. For filing purposes, he headed the note HMA v James Ronald Robertson, as if by habit. As usual – and borne of good practice – it gave the client or the witness time to settle.

Looking up, he saw that she appeared relaxed but more pensive than she had been in the Saltmarket's witness waiting room. She responded to him by forcing a half-smile which quickly dissipated when Dowdall spoke.

'How are the children?'

The slight smile briefly returned. 'They have been brave little souls throughout it all, even when James was sentenced. In an odd way, he had taught them to deal calmly with life's problems. He must be proud of them.'

Dowdall took time to digest her words. *He must be proud of them* ringing out as if the children's father was still of this life, just out working and keeping order somewhere on Southern Division's beat number eight. Or perhaps Janice was simply espousing her husband's unshakably-held belief that God was presently keeping a watchful eye over them from above.

Continuing the theme, Dowdall decided to take a chance. 'He must surely be proud of you too.' Seeing her reaction, he began to regret his words. Her eyes narrowed as she staved off painful thoughts, raw with chafed good intention.

Restraining tears, she took a deep breath before answering. 'I'm sure he is. I should tell you, Mr Dowdall, that whilst I obviously went along with my husband's convictions about God and sometimes accompanied him to certain meetings when I had to, I never fully espoused the Brethren's principles. As you know, he was my first cousin, and we knew each other well before we got married. James and I agreed to disagree as long as he was able to believe that I was doing my best to come to terms with the strictures his church imposed on our lives and that the children would automatically follow on. I still don't know why he refused to let me help though, when he really needed it, God aside. I heard that Brother Ernest paid him a visit. Perhaps it had something to do with that. They're not keen on women doing that much apart from serving tea.'

The answer made him think. From a practical, legal point of view, that did not explain a lot. There was now no point in debating anything with Janice – it was too late and she had tried her best – but surely it would still have been God's will if her husband had relented and agreed to her taking an oath to Him to tell the court her side of the Robertson saga? Or was Robertson simply being protective of his church?

Dowdall decided to take the easy option, the one that would only partially explain his deceased client's eccentric behaviour but would intrigue him until he too passed away. 'James was anxious not to let you and the children down publicly and I assured him he hadn't.' He knew that sounded too shallow to be absolutely true, but it was the best he could come up with in the present situation. *No, he didn't let you down, did he? He just cheated continually with a needy woman then killed her in cold blood.*

And Janice was far too intelligent to fall for something as facile as that. He could even tell by her face that she was disappointed that he had even offered such an explanation, despite it being the one the client wanted him and others to believe. Still, she obviously knew what her husband had been like and played along with the fiction, for now at any rate.

'No, I suppose he didn't,' Janice muttered unconvincingly.

Dowdall felt it was time for him to lighten her load if he could. 'You once mentioned you have a sister in North America. Do you still plan to pay her a visit?'

Janice brightened up, superficially at least. 'Yes, she's been very understanding about all of this. We write constantly by air mail and she and her husband have arranged for the children to attend the same school as their cousin, so we're emigrating in six weeks. They've got me a little house in a decent neighbourhood near to where they stay. It would be silly of me to carry on living here now and the children would always have the ghost of this in their lives, which I don't want for them.'

Dowdall began to feel genuine admiration for this heart-broken, innocent, resourceful young woman who was, without rancour, making best of a uniquely appalling state of affairs whilst presently revealing the plans she harboured to try to save what was left of her shattered home life. There was absolutely no sign of what would have been understandable self-pity in her voice or her manner, just a firm resolve to do what was right by the children. Not for the first time, Dowdall's sympathy, together with a protective urge came to the fore in his dealings with his former client's wife, now widow.

'In that case, what I have to tell you next might be of some minor assistance in the important step you are proposing to take.'

Not attuned to positive news in recent times, Janice looked confused.

Dowdall continued. 'As you may be aware – although you have had enough to cope with recently – my services and that of both senior and junior counsel were given freely …'

She looked surprised, faintly rattled lest he was seeking payment from her as his former client's next of kin.

He spoke quickly to put her mind at ease.

'Please don't think I'm about to land you with a bill, my dear! On the contrary, I have to tell you that a whip round by members of the City of Glasgow Police raised the sum of £500 towards the legal expenses of the case and that a further, similar amount has been raised by public subscription. Despite everything reported in the newspapers, there are still good-hearted folk out there.'

What he didn't say to her was that counsel had been offered some of the cash towards their expenses and had turned it down. Dowdall somewhat reluctantly felt obliged to follow suit despite his legal firm being well out of pocket at the end of the case.

'The consensus is that you and your children should be the recipients of the money.'

Janice's eyes widened at the news. She had a brief moment of hesitation before finally accepting the heavy buff-coloured envelope he handed across the desk. For the first time since he had met her – in this very room, in the depths of a cruel winter's evening – Janice appeared encouraged. She was both polite and gracious in accepting the cash. Dowdall mused it was about to be put to better use than helping his firm bridge the temporary expenditure gap that had developed during his unremunerated work on the case; it had been a financial lull which he had already made up for by his usual diligence and unremitting hard work.

Her face flushed with pleasant discomfort as she she struggled to express her gratitude. 'Mr Dowdall, it's far too early for me to say the children and I will ever recover from this, but whether I do or not doesn't really matter as long as the children do. Words can't express how much I appreciate all the effort you and Mr Cameron and Mr Kissen put into trying to save James.'

He let it remain unsaid, but thought she might complete the sentence correctly by adding 'from himself'.

Who knew what awaited her in a new country? He really wanted to tell her to keep in touch but stopped himself from expressing such a genuine but artificial sounding sentiment. She stood up and proffered her hand which Dowdall grasped gently and bid her farewell. She turned to go, Dowdall following her out.

Then she turned and spoke again. 'I'm sorry Mr Dowdall, I forgot, but would you be kind enough to take care of this?' She went into her handbag and produced a formal looking letter. It was from the Home Office and gave notice that although her husband's meagre possessions were subject to confiscation, they had somehow condescended to return them to her if she would be so kind as to arrange to uplift them from HMP Barlinnie. In effect, the state was content with retaining her husband's body alongside Lyons, Carraher and the others mouldering in the unhallowed, perpetually alien prison grounds, but was apparently prepared to show abnormal compassion in returning a ten-shilling note, a florin, a sixpenny piece, two collar studs, one silver coloured watch of indeterminate make with a worn leather strap and one (Yale) house key for the use of. Dowdall later got Evelyn to write to the prison authorities to let them know that his firm had been instructed by Mrs Janice Robertson to seek the return of her husband's property.

Then life got in the way, and he forgot to follow up the reply from the governor, noting the firm's mandate.

Gorbals life went on as it always had, house-proud owners and hopeless anti-social tenants living side by side as well as those trying to get out at the first opportunity. Although haunted by the vision of Robertson's last moments, Dowdall necessarily moved on and submerged himself in other clients' troubles. Even after several months had gone by, he sometimes found himself puzzling why Robertson had chosen to turn his back on any hope of earthly survival by doing what he did and rejecting his advice. Was it some sort of pointless gesture designed to assure his kids that their father had never actually slipped from the high standards he himself had preached and insisted upon at home? If so, he hadn't even convinced a majority of the fifteen strangers who saw through his flimsy fib and voted for him to die, let alone the sceptical newspaper-reading public. So, why did he privately admit he had been seeing Katie on the side yet deny it when it truly mattered in his evidence? At that stage, the best Dowdall could come up with was that his former client must have had something like a death wish.

It turned out he was almost on the right track without realising it.

One hot summer's day, just after the second anniversary of Katie's murder, officer Philips noticed Dowdall signing in at the prison gate on his way in to seeing another client. He waited until the lawyer was making his way back out of the prison before approaching him in the car park.

'Mr Dowdall,' he said cheerily, his hand extended towards him, 'Remember me?'

Dowdall instantly did so, clasping and shaking other man's hand. 'Of course, I do. How can either of us forget James Ronald Robertson?'

'It was unprofessional of me I know, but I couldn't help feeling sorry for your client. He was a most improbable man to end up lying where he is outside D Hall. It was as if he wanted to go. I always promised myself I would tell you this if I had the chance. After that last meeting you had with him, his whole character changed and he looked and sounded relieved because you agreed with him about something, but he never told me what it was. You know, in those last few days he talked about you a lot because he valued your opinion so much.'

With profoundly mixed feelings, Dowdall recalled what he and Robertson had said at that surreal final appointment. 'Now he's gone, I can tell you I assured him – as much as I was able to – that he had not let his family down in public. He seemed to take some comfort in that.'

'Whatever you said, it certainly worked. How often can it be said that the condemned man was also a contented man?'

Dowdall was strangely pleased to hear it. 'You know, on behalf of his widow I always meant to reclaim his possessions but never got round to it. It's one of things you always find excuses not to do.'

'I can understand that. Funnily enough …' Philips reached into his pocket and produced a receipt and a small packet with a clear, see-through window. 'I brought this out to you thinking it wouldn't be right for them to just lie there forever unclaimed. I hope you don't mind.'

'Of course, I don't. Thank you for doing that.' Dowdall took the packet then signed the receipt which Philips then placed in his tunic pocket and turned to go.

He stopped a few feet away, turned back and added, 'Oh, there's something else in the bag which strictly speaking might not be classed as one of his possessions. You'll also find some folded foolscap pages in his handwriting which I decided to keep. He asked for writing paper and I gave him a pen, although I wasn't meant to, and he sat writing it out. I had a look at it but couldn't really make out much beyond him making peace with his maker. See what you think.'

Dowdall agreed that he would, as yet unsure what he was going to do with the items apart from holding on to them as painful reminders, should Janice ever get back in touch and prefer not to claim them.

Philips had more to say. 'One more thing. His grave keeps sinking, no matter what we do to it. It looks like it might be due to water ingress and, oddly enough, it's only his that's affected. We've tried using ashes and fresh tarmac but it keeps slipping down. It's as if he's trying to get away from Lyons, Carraher and the others!'

The day Philips gave Dowdall Robertson's earthly goods, he'd taken them back to the office, and without opening put them in a large white envelope, appending his initials on the front and placing it into the small office safe, the one used for 'spill-over' deeds and wills. In the months and years following, particularly when he was alone and working late, he often thought he might retrieve it for old time's sake, but it was always too soon, his feelings still too raw. Every time he thought of opening it, he decided not to because of the bittersweet conflict it brought; like re-reading a loved one's final diary entry or hesitating to open a drawer, knowing a long dead parent's prized watch or cherished dog-eared bible could be in it, waiting.

Five years after Katie's murder, the office manager left the envelope on his desk along with a note explaining that the conveyancing partner had ordered a clear out of the office safes. Dowdall got the note and the envelope when he returned from court after office hours, the note ending *I've checked with the others and they all say this must be yours. It hasn't been opened. I'll check with you tomorrow. As Mrs D always says, try not to work too late as your dinner's on the table! Goodnight, Evelyn.*

Dowdall sat for a while, harrowing memories and images flooding his brain. Katie's naïve efforts to improve her and her children's lot in life ending in tragedy, John Cameron's grit and determination to see an increasingly hopeless cause through to an inevitably catastrophic end, but above all, the last agonising image of a hapless Robertson turning to attempt a final wave as if he was bidding farewell to an anxious parent at the gates of a school.

With deep misgivings, he picked up a stubby silver letter opener and sliced the envelope's yellowing calico covering, emptying its contents onto his desk. The see-through section of the packet inside was clinging to some other paper with the combination of air and condensation – perhaps a reminder from the client that the passage of time is swift, and wasting it is a sin. He prised the packet's edges from each other, releasing a musty, leathery aroma. He painstakingly picked out all the items and placed them in a row on the worn leather desk inlay in front of him.

All the things on the property list were there, but, the handwritten pages had not been logged as being part of the executed man's property, just as Philips had said.

His hand trembling slightly, Dowdall read his former client's final written words. As he did so, he felt he began to get a clearer picture of why he had done what he had in the witness box the following day. It read like a prayer, as if Robertson was scripting something to be recited when needed.

The pages flowed in a steady copperplate hand. It read:

The Condemned Cell
D Hall
Barlinnie Prison
Glasgow
15th December 1950

Lord,

My earthly journey ends and my redemption begins tomorrow. You have sorely tested me, but I think I have achieved all you have asked of me. In your wisdom you made me carry out your work in a depraved and evil place amongst unworthy people and as your disciple I followed your teachings with an uplifted heart. As you gave your only son to die on the cross at Golgotha in vicarious atonement for our sins, I give my life on the scaffold here tomorrow to save my soul and to rid this evil world of the wicked and ungodly body you saw fit to test me in.

Grant me eternal salvation in sacrificing my mortal being to rid this immoral and sinful world of another who dwells inside me; one who has no regard for mankind's flawed and temporal laws and yet understands that your law is eternal.

Lord hear my prayer.

Your unworthy servant

It was signed 'James Robertson' in a clear, steady hand. There was no mention of his middle name.

Epilogue

If Robertson's widow is still alive, perhaps she has also heard of the disappearance and murder of 33-year-old Sarah Everard, who went missing on the night of the 3rd March 2021 whilst walking home to Brixton Hill from a friend's house near Clapham Common in London. Her body was discovered a week later in Kent, the day after 48-year-old Wayne Couzens was arrested on suspicion of her kidnap, then her murder. The revelation that Couzens was a serving Metropolitan Police officer at the time of the alleged offences served to heighten anger about women being unable to safely walk the streets at night without fear of harassment or violence. A vigil for the murdered woman in Clapham Common on 13th March 2021 was controversially broken up by former colleagues of the accused man – officers of the Metropolitan Police – on the basis that the attendees were risking the spread of Covid 19. Couzens was sacked by the Metropolitan Police following his guilty plea on 9th July 2021 to murdering Sarah, and is due to be sentenced on 29th September 2021.

It's not known if Robertson's widow ever did contact Dowdall again, although he often thought of her down the years. She had seemed resigned rather than bitter about her husband's self-appointed role as protector of his family's morals, thinking he had saved them from the perils of living in an evil world – never fully recognising how much he was blinded to his own hypocrisy by his own beliefs.

At the time of Robertson's execution, the recommendations of the Royal Commission on Capital Punishment were still years away, one of which was installing rubber cushions to soften the macabre, foreboding crash of the weighted sack in rehearsal the day before the scheduled date, reminding the prisoner in the next cell that tomorrow his body would replace the practice sack. Perhaps the noise of the hangman's preparations was regarded as part of a prisoner's punishment? Ten years after Robertson was hanged, a new Chief Constable of the City of Glasgow Police was appointed. His name? James Robertson. Perhaps for his own reasons, he saw fit to distinguish himself from James Ronald Robertson by designing himself as 'Chief Constable James A Robertson'.

Dowdall himself passed away in 1995 at the age of 90. He rarely talked about the Robertson case, although it was included in his memoirs *Get Me Dowdall!* – the title taken from the reputed demand of the newly arrested throughout the land. In his memoir, he made no connection with James Hogg's *The Private Memoirs and Confessions of a Justified Sinner,* once described as 'The devil's subtle conquest of a self-righteous man.' It's an allegorical tale of religious zealotry in the course of which anything – even murder – can be said to be divinely decreed if the perpetrator is preordained to salvation. The anti-hero, like Robertson, died with a rope around his neck and was interred in a waterlogged grave. His exhumed body was described by James Hogg in 'excellent broad Scotch' thus: '*I hae often wondered how it was that this man's corpse has been miraculously preserved fae decay, a hunder times langer than any other body's, or even a tanner's.*'

Eerily, as the years rolled on, Robertson's grave continually sank, despite efforts to shore it up. At one stage, as work was being carried out on the grounds, a flap in the coffin was opened, and officers and prisoners passing on a work detail were both horrified and mesmerised by how well preserved his face had remained. Despite the quicklime and water used in his burial – then thought to hasten the decomposition process – he was still recognisable. Why had they bothered? Was Eternity not happening soon enough?

Studies now show that quicklime actually slows the rate of decomposition. In 2020, the Scottish Prison Service announced plans to build a new facility, about a mile or so from where Barlinnie has stood since 1882. It's to be known as 'Her Majesty's Prison Glasgow', a name which surely cannot be corrupted in the same way that Barlinnie has by a macho, cowboy ranch mentality that led to it being universally known as 'The Bar-L'. No doubt time will prove this statement wrong. As Barlinnie has to go, the plans for demolition must include a treatment of what will happen to the remains of the ten men who were hanged there between 1946 and 1960. The suggestion is that this task be done 'considerately' – and should the relatives of the executed men wish to, they can reclaim what's left of their ancestor's bodies and supervise of their disposal as they see fit. Could the earthly remains of James Ronald Robertson yet reside in consecrated ground?

Rumour had it that right up to his final moments, Robertson fully expected a last-minute reprieve, but that never seems to have been Dowdall's view. He reasoned that Robertson had gambled and lost – fully aware that his life would be forfeit – rather than admit he had fathered a child with a mistress – implicitly from the wrong side of the tracks – all to save his wife and children from public shame. As an explanation and as a tactic, that theory has its limitations. By the trial's end, the entire world already knew the truth – so can there be another reason? Perhaps someone like James Hogg, known as 'The Ettrick Shepherd', might have understood the mind of James Ronald Robertson, one-time City of Glasgow police officer, 138D, formerly of beat number eight in the city's Southern Division. Hogg wrote:

'But in this day and with the present generation, it will not go down that a man should be daily tempted by the Devil

in the semblance of a fellow creature; and at length lured to self-destruction in the hopes that this same fiend and tormentor was to suffer and fall along with him ...'

What if the experienced officer from the Traffic Department, Kevan, had not been suspicious of what he saw when he attended the scene at Prospecthill Road in the early hours of 28th July 1950? To the untrained eye, it had all the hallmarks of a straightforward road traffic accident; even some of the police in attendance that morning failed to appreciate the signs of something more sinister than a pedestrian being the victim of a hit and run. With no obvious point of impact and the curious pattern of the bloody tyre marks on the road surface, the incident was quickly spotted for what it really was. Even so, it would still have been a long shot for the whole thing to have been swept under the carpet and for Robertson to have simply resumed a routine, mistress-free family life. Would he, and *could* he have done that? Given that he effectively signed his own death warrant in the witness box – causing speculation ever since – it must be wondered if he would or even could have picked up the threads of the life he lived before the murder. Might he have committed further major crimes to seek punishment from above? Or did one sin simply bring on another and so on, adultery leading to theft, which led to murder? A sheep or a lamb, what difference does it make?

We'll never know.

Bibliography and Sources

Abbot, G. *William Calcraft Executioner Extra-ordinaire* (Eric Dobby Publishing, 2004)

Dowdall, L. with Marshall, A. *Get Me Dowdall!* (Paul Harris Publishing, 1979)

Eunson, E. *The Gorbals: An Illustrated History* (Richard Stenlake Publishing, 1996)

Glaister, J. *Final Diagnosis* (Hutchinson & Co., 1964)

House, J. *Square Mile of Murder* (Richard Drew Publishing Limited, 1988)

Knox, B. *Court of Murder* (John Long Ltd., 1968)

Hogg, J. *The Private Memoirs and Confessions of a Justified Sinner* (Wordsworth Editions Limited, 2003)

Pierrepoint, A. *Executioner: Pierrepoint* (Coronet Books/ Hodder and Stoughton, 1977)

Other Sources

The Glasgow Herald
The Bulletin and Scots Pictorial
The Daily Record
Hanging with Frank, dir. by David Graham Scott (Vimeo/ YouTube, 1995)
Liberation dir. by Martyn Bennett (Real World, 2003)

About the Author

Allan MacKenzie Nicol was born in Buckie but grew up in Drumchapel and Scotstoun in Glasgow. After qualifying as a Solicitor, he joined the Crown Office and became a Procurator Fiscal Depute for 12 years. He qualified as an Advocate in 1993 and then defended clients charged with more serious offences until 2011, when he re-joined the Crown Office and became an Advocate Depute, prosecuting in High Courts throughout Scotland.

His previous work, *Manuel: Scotland's First Serial Killer* and *The Monster Butler* is published by Black & White Publishing. He wrote *Manuel: Scotland's First Serial Killer* in 2008; the second edition appearing in 2016 and coinciding with the television series *In Plain Sight*, for which he was script adviser.

'Perhaps it's the combination of law and history that attracts me to trials from the past,' he writes, 'at best, they are reconstructions of events that reveal a small percentage of the story.'

Ringwood Publishing

All titles are available from the Ringwood website in both print and ebook format, as well as from usual outlets.

www.ringwoodpublishing.com

mail@ringwoodpublishing.com

Clutching at Straws
Charles P. Sharkey

Clutching At Straws is a gritty and realistic dive into Glasgow's criminal underworld. The novel follows Inspector Frank Dorsey and his partner DC George Mitchell as they investigate a dead body they believe to be linked to the Moffats, one of the most notorious crime families in Glasgow. However, as they begin to delve further into the case, it becomes apparent that they have a complex web of connected mysteries and murders to make sense of.

ISBN: 978-1-901514-72-8

£9.99

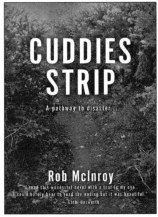

ISBN: 978-1-901514-88-9

£9.99

Cuddies Strip
Rob McInroy

Cuddies Strip is based on a true crime and faithfully follows the investigation and subsequent trial but it also examines the mores of the times and the insensitive treatment of women in a male-dominated society.

It is a highly absorbing period piece from 1930s Scotland, with strong contemporary resonances: both about the nature and responsiveness of police services and the ingrained misogyny of the whole criminal justice system.

Ruxton - The First Modern Murder
Tom Wood

It is 1935 and the deaths of Isabella Ruxton and Mary Rogerson would result in one of the most complex investigations the world had ever seen. The gruesome murders captured worldwide attention with newspapers keeping the public enthralled with all the gory details.

But behind the headlines was a different, more important story: the ground-breaking work of Scottish forensic scientists who developed new techniques to solve the case and shape the future of scientific criminal investigation.

ISBN: 978-1-901514-84-1
£9.99

Murder at the Mela
Leela Soma

DI Alok Patel takes the helm of an investigation into the brutal murder of an Asian woman in this eagerly-awaited thriller. As Glasgow's first Asian DI, Patel faces prejudice from his colleagues and suspicion from the Asian community as he struggles with the pressure of his rank, relationships, and racism.

This murder-mystery explores not just the hate that lurks in the darkest corners of Glasgow, but the hate which exists in the very streets we walk.

ISBN: 978-1-901514-90-2
£9.99

Not the Life Imagined
Anne Pettigrew

A darkly humorous, thought-provoking story of Scottish medical students in the sixties, a time of changing social and sexual mores. None of the teenagers starting at Glasgow University in 1967 live the life they imagine.

In *Not the Life Imagined*, retired medic Anne Pettigrew tells a tale of ambition and prejudice that provides a humorous and compelling insight into the complex dynamics of the NHS fifty years ago.

ISBN: 978-1-901514-70-4

£9.99

ISBN: 978-1-901514-80-3

£9.99

Not the Deaths Imagined
Anne Pettigrew

In a leafy Glasgow suburb, Dr Beth Semple is busy juggling motherhood and full-time GP work in the 90s NHS. But her life becomes even more problematic when she notices some odd deaths in her neighbourhood. Though Beth believes the stories don't add up, the authorities remain stubbornly unconvinced.

Is a charming local GP actually a serial killer? Can Beth piece together the jigsaw of perplexing fatalities and perhaps save lives? And as events accelerate towards a dramatic conclusion, will the police intervene in time?